"A virgin?

"Are we back to that again?" Her anger returned full force. "What do you want me to do, apologise? Say I'm sorry I haven't been to bed with every guy that came along?"

"Damn it, Shiloh—"

She cut him off acidly. "Nice double standard you use, McQuade. Tell you what. I'll just go find someone without your scruples!"

"Shut up!" Con snapped. The idea of her making love with someone else was painful.

"Why? Just because you don't want me doesn't mean somebody else won't someday." She took in a gulp of air, ashamed of herself but unable to stop. "Some-body who isn't all bogged down in what they think I want . . . " Her words faded as she stared at him. "Do you think I'll lay some kind of claim on you? That I'll expect you to . . . to make an honest woman of me or something?"

Dear Reader:

We at Silhouette are very excited to bring you this reading **Sensation**. *Look out for the four books which appear in our* **Silhouette Sensation** *series every month. These stories will have the high quality you have come to expect from Silhouette, and their varied and provocative plots will encourage you to explore the wonder of falling in love – again and again!*

Emotions run high in these drama-filled novels. Greater sensual detail and an extra edge of realism intensify the hero and heroine's relationship so that you cannot help but be caught up in their every change of mood.

We hope you enjoy this **Sensation** *– and will go on to enjoy many more.*

We would love to hear your comments and encourage you to write to us:

Jane Nicholls
Silhouette Books
PO Box 236
Thornton Road
Croydon
Surrey
CR9 3RU

JUSTINE DAVIS
Cool Under Fire

Silhouette Sensation

First published in Great Britain in 1993
by Silhouette Books, Eton House, 18-24 Paradise Road,
Richmond, Surrey TW9 1SR

© Janice Davis Smith 1992

Silhouette, Silhouette Sensation and Colophon are
Trade Marks of Harlequin Enterprises B.V.

ISBN 0 373 58796 1

18-9305

Made and printed in Great Britain

Other novels by Justine Davis

Silhouette Sensation

Hunter's Way
Stevie's Chase

Silhouette Desire

Angel for Hire
Upon the Storm

For Carla—
My dear friend who, with an unquenchable spirit,
personifies "cool under fire."

Chapter 1

Shiloh had read the phrase "his jaw dropped," but she'd doubted that it ever really happened. She knew better now as she stared openmouthed at the sight before her. The crew, who said nothing ever ruffled her, would love to get a look at her now, she thought.

There was a man in her bed. Or, actually, on it, face-down, sprawled crosswise in a way that gave her a clue as to his height; the five-foot width of her queen-size brass bed was more than a foot short of holding him. And she had no idea who he was.

At least, she didn't think so. True, she couldn't see his face, because it was buried in the crook of the arm that cushioned his head and partly masked by the tousled, slightly long mane of dark hair, but she was reasonably sure that that body did not belong to anyone she knew. And she certainly could see enough of it to judge, she thought, wishing her heart would recover from the shock and slow down.

Only a pair of light blue briefs broke the long, tanned length of that body, leaving the lean, muscular lines of strong legs, narrow hips and waist, and broad back and shoulders bare to her gaze. And what that band of cloth did cover was just as interesting; the tight, muscled swell of his buttocks made her fingers curl.

What are you doing? she snapped at herself, backing up a step. Why aren't you on the phone to the police? You walk in on a total stranger lying half—no, make that nine-tenths—naked on your bed, and instead of doing the rational thing and screaming your lungs out, you're taking inventory. They're right; you *are* strange.

But why was there no sign that her house had been broken into? Not a thing out of place, nothing that wasn't as she'd left it, except for the pile of clothes on the floor and their owner on her bed. Could it just be some kind of mix-up? A case of mistaken address?

Call the police, idiot, she told herself, and tiptoed past the sprawled man to the bedside phone. A muffled sound stopped her in her tracks, and she froze as the man lifted his head and looked unerringly straight at her, as if he'd known where she was all the time. She had barely registered that he had vivid, heavily lashed blue eyes before he murmured something, so low and soft that she almost missed it.

"You're . . . prettier than . . . picture."

As if those few words had sapped the last of his failing strength, his head fell back on his arm.

Picture? What picture? Where on earth had he seen a picture of her? She stared down at the prone figure, her mind whirling. She now knew without a doubt that she had never seen this man before. Even if she had been stricken with amnesia and forgotten that incredible body, nothing on earth could have made her forget those eyes.

But he knew her. Or thought he did, she amended, but he couldn't, not really. But what picture could he be talking about?

"Hey," she said tentatively. No response. She tried again. Nothing. He just lay there, ignoring her. She reached out to shake him, conscious with a little rush of abashment that she was scrupulously avoiding touching anything other than his bare arm.

When she did, she recoiled instantly. "My God," she whispered, her fingers still tingling from the heat of him. It was then that something else about those eyes finally penetrated her racing thoughts. They had been searingly blue, but they had also been bright and hot with the glitter of fever.

Wonderful. She had hoped that this was all some elaborate joke, planned and carried out by that bunch of clowns she worked with, who seemed on an unceasing mission to shatter what they called her unnatural calm. The first touch of her fingers on that fevered skin singed that idea to ashes.

Call the paramedics, she muttered, nodding to herself at the reasonableness of the idea. Have them cart him away and solve both the problem of his presence and his obvious illness. She reached for the phone.

"Shy..."

She jerked around. Had she heard it? Or had it just been a suppressed, fevered moan that sounded like her name?

"Damn." It slipped out, startling her. "I wish you would wake up!"

In answer he only rolled over, making his head loll back uncomfortably over the edge of the bed. Great, she muttered inwardly, the front looks better than the back.

Her eyes were drawn to a puckered ridge of flesh above his right hip, an angry, wicked-looking scar that began just above the bone and wrapped halfway around his side. And then to another, this one a smooth, white line curving from the top of his left shoulder down over his collarbone and across the top of his chest, stopping just short of the breastbone. On the smooth, tanned skin of that muscled chest, with no mass of concealing hair to hide it, the thin line stood out starkly through the sheen of fevered sweat.

Lord, she breathed, who was this man who had dropped out of nowhere, shaking her vaunted calm? She raised a hand to rub the back of her neck, lifting the thick, necklength sweep of burnished auburn hair. When she realized she was responding to the awkward angle of his neck, not a real pain in hers, she knew she couldn't just let him stay like that.

As soon as she moved, the self-possession that had momentarily deserted her returned. She wrestled with the solid bulk of him, levering and pushing and pulling, then tugging at the covers until he was beneath them. He barely stirred, moaning only once, a low, raspy sound that he seemed to try to stop even though he was clearly beyond being aware of it.

He looked pale somehow, even beneath his tan. And she could see now that dark circles shadowed his eyes beneath the thick fringe of lashes. Oddly, his jaw seemed set and tight despite his oblivion; it was strong, firm and very determined.

She also saw, when his sweat-dampened hair fell back as she slipped a pillow behind his head, another scar, a small crease of whitened flesh that began an inch below the hairline and disappeared into the thick darkness. It did nothing to lessen her unease, although she continued to work dispassionately.

With the thought that she should call the paramedics still in the back of her mind, she walked to the bathroom to get the thermometer. She could at least find out how high his fever really was first. And she could get a cool cloth while she was at it, and sponge him off a little.

When she picked up the phone a few minutes later, holding the thermometer that read 103 degrees, instead of calling 911 for the paramedics and an ambulance, she found herself dialing a completely different number.

"Dr. Watterson's office."

"Mandy?"

"Is that you, Shy? How are you?" Amanda Wilcox sounded genuinely pleased to hear from her.

"Fine. Er, sort of. How serious is a 103-degree temperature?"

"Oh, no, not you, too? It's everywhere, but you're the last one I expected. You never get sick!"

Shiloh didn't challenge her assumption. "What is it?"

"Some kind of viral infection. We're going crazy here, but I can find room for you if you want to come in. We're going to be running late, anyway."

"Would it do any good?"

"Not really," the young nurse answered honestly. "Antibiotics don't seem to have that much effect, and the doctor is basically telling everyone who isn't under ten or over sixty to stay in bed and take aspirin and—"

"—plenty of liquids. I know the drill. Will it get worse?"

"It pretty much knocks people for a loop if they get it bad. If they're run-down in the first place, it can get pretty serious, but it usually only lasts a couple of days. Just long enough to ruin your weekend," Mandy teased, then became serious again. "Do you want me to stop by when I get off?"

"No," Shiloh said quickly, "that's all right."

"I don't like to think of you there alone if you have a bad case."

"I . . . I'll be fine."

"Well, if you're sure. But if the fever hasn't dropped by tomorrow, you come in. It's so bad we're opening up for a few hours in the morning. Take care, Shy."

"Thanks, Mandy."

Now what? she wondered as she hung up. She leaned over to check the cool washcloth she'd placed on his forehead. She glanced at her watch. Five-thirty. She would wait awhile, she thought. If he wasn't any better by later tonight, she would call for help. She couldn't quite understand why she didn't call now, only that something held her back.

It couldn't be just coincidence, she thought, that this man who knew her name had wound up in her house. He had intended to come, had expected her to be here. And had recognized her when he had seen her, even half out of his head with fever.

A vague image from her childhood, of a man appearing on their doorstep in the dark of night, nudged at Shiloh's mind. Her father had taken him in, whispering to her only that he was someone who needed help.

"He's your friend, Daddy?" she'd asked.

"In a way, baby, even though I don't know him."

Her young mind hadn't worked through to understanding what her father had meant until much later, but the memory of the event had stayed with her. Now this man clearly needed help. And although in leaving home she'd also left the kind of life that brought strangers to the door, she'd never left behind her father's example. She would let him stay, she thought, until she found out if he, too, was a friend even though she didn't know him. And in the meantime, she would be extremely wary.

In between changing her clothes, fixing herself a meal and sorting her mail, she kept rewetting the cloth, which seemed to become warm from his skin as fast as she could rinse it out. She swabbed his face, arms and chest, trying not to notice how he stirred, how the flat, brown discs of his nipples tautened when the rough, cool cloth swept over them. At last she pulled up the wicker lounge from beside the fireplace and stretched out on it, tilting the shade on the nightstand lamp so that its glow fell on the pages of the book she'd picked up and the face of the man in the bed was cast into shadow.

It didn't matter. She could still see each feature as if it were lit by a spotlight. Even with that jaw shadowed by a couple of days of beard growth, it was a clean, chiseled face that was saved from rugged harshness by the thick, long sweep of his lashes and the softer line of his mouth. Who was he? She ordered herself to stop thinking about him; she would find out when he woke up, and not before.

She'd thought of going through his clothes, looking for something to identify him, but it seemed such a violation while he lay there helpless that she couldn't bring herself to do it. If she had to call the paramedics, they could do it. Right, she thought with a grimace, while you explain what this man you've never laid eyes on before is doing in your house. In your bed.

She came awake with a start and glanced automatically at the clock on the nightstand. Her eyes widened; she hadn't meant to doze off, let alone sleep for hours. She shifted her gaze to the bed; he seemed to be sleeping peacefully. She got up and reached for the washcloth she'd left folded over his forehead.

Without warning she was flying through the air, a crushing grip around her wrists. In a bare instant she was flat on her back, a hard, muscled weight pinning her to the bed, that iron grip forcing her hands above her head. She smothered the scream that rose in her throat, trying to channel her panic into an effort to break free.

The man above her stopped dead. Incongruously, she found herself wondering at the rapid-fire changes that raced across his rugged face, from the relative peace and vulnerability of sleep to instant, violent alertness and hair-trigger reaction, which were replaced just as quickly by something else. The deadly chill in his piercing blue eyes faded, to be replaced by awareness and, she realized, recognition. He knew her. She didn't know how or why, but he knew her.

She didn't know if that eased or added to her fear. She held his gaze despite every instinct that was crying out for her to get away. Something akin to admiration flashed briefly in his blue eyes, and then he abruptly rolled off her.

"Sorry," he muttered, an arm rising to rest over his eyes, as if even the dim light of the room were painful.

Shiloh's eyebrows shot up. Sorry? He breaks into my house, takes up residence on my bed, then, when I'm only trying to help him, pounces on me like . . . like . . .

Like she didn't know what. She couldn't think of anything right now that moved that fast. And if this was what he was like when he was sick, Lord help anyone who got in his way when he wasn't.

He had ruptured her perennial calm, had frightened her out of her hard-won serenity, and all she got was a grudging "Sorry"? In place of her initial panic another emotion was growing: anger. She climbed over him to stand beside the bed, being none too careful about where she put her hands and knees; she heard him grunt and saw the arm lift abruptly from his eyes when her knee used his stomach for leverage.

Tough, she thought. It was hard as a rock, anyway; she was surprised he'd felt it at all. She glared down at him.

She'd had just about enough of this. She reached for the phone. He reacted as swiftly as before, his hand darting out to clasp her wrist once more, but she was half expecting it this time. She grabbed the receiver and rapped it across his knuckles fiercely.

"Damn."

He swore under his breath as he yanked his hand back, but that odd flash of admiration came again, this time mixed with a rather rueful look she didn't at all understand. Nor did she try to analyze the strangeness of it right now.

She backed up a step and shifted the phone in her hands so she could dial. He struggled to sit up, and she had to steel herself against the sight of how hard it was for him. The taut, whipcord muscles and the lean, hard body told her this was not a man used to weakness. She could sense his frustration as he fell back.

"Don't."

He didn't shout, he didn't snap, but it was an order nevertheless. She ignored it, although something in his voice made her uneasy. It was low and had the rasp of a raw throat, yet it held the note of a man who was used to being obeyed. Instantly.

Tough, she repeated to herself. She dialed the nine and moved to the one.

"Please."

She paused. He'd said it between gritted teeth, and it didn't take much intuition to know that it was not something he said frequently. More used to ordering than asking, she thought as she lifted her head to look at him.

"Give me one good reason why," she said, anger making her tone icy.

He closed his eyes, letting out a short breath that she suspected would have been a groan if he wasn't so determined to disguise how rotten he was feeling. "Just don't."

Any thawing she might have been experiencing at the sight of his pain halted abruptly at the arrogant words.

"Not good enough." She dialed the first one.

"Shiloh."

She didn't turn a hair. "I've already gathered that you know who I am. But I don't know you, and I don't want you here."

For a third time, that admiring look gleamed in his eyes, but the ruefulness had been replaced with an unexpected gleam of approval. Absurdly it warmed her, which only made her angrier.

"I'll leave."

She looked at him, surprised, although she wasn't sure why, that it had been so easy. And, for a reason she didn't understand, a little disappointed. She hung up before completing the call. "Just like that?"

"Shouldn't have come here in the first place." His words were muffled a little by his efforts to move. Using the closest bedpost, he pulled himself up. Sweat broke out once more on his forehead, and he was moving with agonizing slowness, every muscle taut and strained, but he never stopped.

Shiloh winced inwardly as she watched him struggle to stand up. Whoever he was, he had no business being on his feet. Before she could speak, he leaned over to pick up the pair of faded jeans she had folded over the footboard of the bed, and then, with a small, smothered sound of protest, he crumpled to the floor.

She knelt beside him, turning him over. He mumbled something unintelligible as his head lolled back limply. His skin did not feel as fiercely hot as it had, but clearly he was still very sick. The thought that this might be something more than the virus Mandy Wilcox had told her about had never been far from her mind, and this time she didn't hesitate in picking up the phone.

When she'd hung up she went for the damp cloth again, rinsing it quickly to cool it. She went back and knelt beside him again, drawing the cloth over his forehead. He stirred, murmured again; then the dark lashes fluttered. They lifted, and a pair of dazed blue eyes were looking up at her.

"It's all right," she soothed. "The paramedics are on their way. They'll get you to a hospital—"

"No!"

That dazed look vanished, and with a convulsive effort he sat up, leaning against the side of the bed for support. Shiloh sat back on her heels, her unease returning.

"Call them back," he ordered in a tone made no less intimidating by his obvious weakness. And even though he looked helpless, Shiloh wasn't convinced. Still, after she studied him for a moment, she merely said, "No."

He stared at her, then closed his eyes as what could have been a wry chuckle if he'd had more breath escaped him.

"Stop them, damn it," he grated out.

Shiloh was at the end of her patience with his dictatorial ways. "You have broken into my home, manhandled me and sworn at me," she snapped. "If I'd had any brains, I would have called the police the minute I saw you! But the paramedics can cart you away just as well. I don't care, as long as you're out of here. Soon."

His eyes were open again, watching her. "Shil—"

"Stop it!" So much for calm, she thought in irritation. "I don't know how you found out who I am or where I live, but it's not going to do any good. There's not a single thing you can say that can make me pick up that phone."

His eyes closed again for a brief moment, a look of weary resignation coming over his face. Then, in a low tone that matched the look, he spoke. One single syllable, but it stopped her cold.

"Linc."

Chapter 2

If Connor McQuade had been a less observant man, he might have missed that barely perceptible tightening of her mouth, that half second of shocked motionlessness. But even as ill as he was, his instinct for self-survival told him just how much depended on the next few minutes, and he watched her intently, silently.

She was looking at him reflectively, her expression unreadable now. Then, without saying a word to him, she picked up the phone and dialed. Her voice was calm and neutral as she cancelled the responding paramedics.

She hung up and turned back to him, and in the same careful voice said, "You'd better get back into bed."

Damn, he thought, Linc had said she was a cool customer, but this was incredible. "Just like that?"

"When did you eat last?"

Disconcerted, he tried to think. "Yesterday?"

"Thursday?"

He went a little paler under his tan. "It's...Friday?"

One arched, delicate brow lifted. "Yes. For another hour, anyway."

"Damn," he muttered, his head falling back against the bed. He felt her gaze on him and tried to shrug it off. "I . . . seem to have lost a day." He hadn't known he'd been that sick. Where had he been, what had he done, in that lost time?

"If you haven't eaten, that's probably half the problem. I'll fix something."

He watched her leave the room, amazement growing inside him. Where was the inquisition? The spate of questions he'd expected would follow the name he had so reluctantly used? He'd written off Linc's description as prejudiced at the time, but he couldn't deny now that his old friend had not exaggerated the nerve and coolheadedness of Shiloh Reese.

And he had greatly understated her looks. He'd described her as a feisty, skinny little redhead with freckles on her nose. The freckles were there, barely visible on the sassily tilted nose, but the red hair had deepened to a rich, warm auburn, cut just above her shoulders in a sleek, classic sweep, and if she had once been thin all over, she was certainly filled out in all the right places now.

In the picture he'd seen, she'd been a cute, bright-eyed fourteen-year-old; the woman ten years later was lovely, all female, but just as feisty. She hadn't even screamed when he'd pinned her. She'd just fought him with a strength that had startled him and stared him down without a trace of fear in those emerald eyes.

And walloped him a good one with that damned phone, he thought, rubbing his still sore knuckles. A smile tugged at the corners of his mouth, then died unexpressed as the truth of his own earlier words came to him. He should never have come here in the first place. He had no right to put her at risk, which he easily might already have done. Damn, if he could only remember what he'd done yesterday. . . .

He nearly jumped when she was suddenly there, a steaming mug held on a tray along with a glass of milk. His brow furrowed. Either she moved like a cat or he was really out of it; he should have heard her.

She saw his frown and, setting the tray on the night-stand, said rather coolly, "You don't have much choice about the menu, so I'd suggest you make the best of it."

"No," he said quickly, "I didn't mean… It wasn't that." Boy, you are sick, McQuade. You're floundering around like a schoolboy trying to talk his way out of trouble with the teacher. Taking refuge in motion, he moved his knees to try to get up. He made it halfway before he had to lean against the bed once more.

"That didn't work real well the last time," she said, her voice studiously devoid of sarcasm. "Here." She held out a hand to him, and after a split second's hesitation he took it. She didn't try to pull him up, merely provided a steady leverage point for him to use what strength he had, then helped him balance as he dropped back down on the bed. Briskly she tugged at the covers, tucking them around him without fussing, and he thanked her silently.

She reached for the mug of soup. "Can you hold this?"

A vision of her having to feed him flashed through his mind, oddly disconcerting. "No." He heard how odd he'd sounded, and added quickly, "I mean yes, I can."

She looked at him quizzically but didn't speak as she handed him the steaming cup. His hands were a little unsteady, but he managed to take a swallow, then looked startled as his stomach growled in response.

"Whatever you did yesterday, I'd say it didn't include eating."

"No."

He took another swallow, his dark brows furrowing again. He remembered a place, a dark, damp place, the sound of footsteps and the burning in his lungs as he tried to smother the sound of his own breathing. And he remembered walking. Endlessly, it seemed. But what else?

"Maybe it will come back when you feel better."

He looked up sharply, startled at her perception. Now would come the questions, he thought. But they didn't; she merely picked up and folded the damp washcloth she had been using, he realized now, to cool him down. She'd helped him, nursed him, even before he'd reluctantly dropped that name. And still no questions.

It was beginning to bother him that she didn't ask. There was something almost abnormal about her calm. It was like waiting for the other shoe to drop. Linc's name had been the first; she held the other.

The gaze of those vivid green eyes was unnerving, and he was not a man who was easily unnerved. He told himself it was because he had been expecting a skinny, freckle-faced tomboy and had instead been confronted with a lusciously curved, strikingly beautiful woman. The silence stretched.

He sipped the soup. Now, after the first hasty swallows, he savored the spicy, rich flavor.

"This is good."

He only said it because it was true, he assured himself, not because the silence and that steady gaze were wearing on him. And he said it because there was no other safe topic of conversation; he had a feeling she would see through any dissembling. There was no masking the lively intelligence in those remarkable eyes. He marvelled once again at her cool composure. Any other woman would be frantic, pelting him with questions; she seemed content to wait.

Almost. Those steady emerald eyes were exerting a pressure that was almost tangible and somehow more effective than any of the various blunter and more physical methods of persuasion he'd encountered.

If he was uncomfortable under her unwavering regard, Shiloh couldn't see it. He seemed calm, inscrutable, cool to the point of chilly, but the way he was eating the soup, quietly but with quick, regular movements that spoke of his hunger, belied his exterior calm.

Any explanations, she realized, were going to have to wait until he had some food in him. If then, she thought suddenly, another image of her father, explaining patiently that he'd told her all he could for now, rising in her mind. How many times had she heard it? How many times had it taken before she'd finally quit asking, realizing that he would tell her what he could when he could, and not before?

She watched him eat, telling herself that she could wait; she'd learned her lessons well. He needed food and rest, and then . . . Well, then she would see what happened.

Con was all too aware of her gaze. But his hunger overcame his careful reserve, and when he had finished the soup, he accepted her offer and ate a half-mug more, then the milk. He took the two aspirin she gave him obediently; he was too aware of the feverish ache of his body to dispute his need of them.

He watched as she silently gathered up the tray and dishes, but before she returned, his fatigue overtook him and he slept.

He awoke to the wonderful absence of that dull, fevered ache and the cheerful presence of the morning sun streaming through the window beside the bed. He still felt weak, but so much better that he wasn't about to complain. He even thought he could get up without falling over this time.

He levered himself up on one elbow, then froze as his gaze fell on the wicker lounge a couple of feet away. Shiloh was curled up on it, asleep, her head pillowed on one slim hand, her hair burnished to a warm, living flame by the sunlight pouring across her.

She looked so touchingly young, so innocent, yet the flowing green silk of the robe she wore did little to conceal the slender, feminine contours beneath. His body clenched around a sudden, searing shaft of heat it took him a moment to recognize, so long had it been since he'd felt it. When he realized it was hot, unmitigated desire, his breath died in his throat in stunned shock and disbelief.

No. The word echoed in his head as if he'd spoken it. Oh, no, you don't. Not now, and not her. Especially not her. He almost laughed at the absurdity of it. After years in an emotional deep freeze, one encounter with this little wildcat was threatening to thaw him out like a blowtorch, and at a time when he could least afford it.

Well, he wasn't going to let it happen. He was going to get out of here before the hell he'd been living in this last week somehow sucked her up, too. He never should have come here, he repeated for the third time.

With a slowness that arose as much from his weakness as from the need for silence, he got up. He swayed at first, a little light-headed, but steadied himself with a hand on the brass bedpost.

This room suited her, he thought as he waited for his head to clear: the gleaming brass bed, the thick, fluffy quilt the color of her eyes and the tailored plaid of the curtains at the window. The combination of feminine curves and functional lines was as intriguing as she was.

Knock it off. You're out of here. That annoying little voice of his was becoming more and more vocal this morning. Usually he trusted it implicitly, but it was beginning to irritate him now.

I'm moving already, he responded silently to it as he inched down to the foot of the bed and reached for his clothes. He carried them to the bathroom and eased the door shut before he began to pull them on. He glanced in the mirror, grimacing at the hollow-eyed, unshaven image that stared back at him. He wished he could take a shower, but he didn't want to take the chance of waking her. He wanted to be gone before that. Coward, he thought, even though he knew it was for the best.

He had his jeans pulled on and was about to zip them when an unsettling thought occurred to him. He strained to remember, but all was lost in that feverish haze. He tried to picture himself here, in her room, that night. It would have made sense, he thought; he'd been burning up. What else would he have done but pull off his too warm clothes?

He almost convinced himself, but a brief, searing image of her undressing him sent a surge of heat through him that made the first one seem like a mere spark. You bastard, he muttered silently, tugging up the jeans zipper and then yanking the blue cotton sweater over his head. A brief spell of dizziness warned him he wasn't yet ready for such quick motions, and he had to stop for a minute until it passed.

He tiptoed to the kitchen, battered leather running shoes in hand, finding his way with an ease that told him the well-trained part of his mind had been functioning and had marked the layout of the house even through the fog of illness.

He quickly checked the shelves and the refrigerator, grabbing a few things that seemed portable. He was under no illusion that he could keep going without food, but he knew he didn't dare risk a restaurant or even a supermarket, not yet. He would leave her some money for what he took, he thought; that, at least, was in good supply. He wished he could leave her a note to thank her, but he didn't dare.

He reached for his wallet, then stopped, hand poised over his hip pocket. Had she? He pulled it out slowly. It didn't matter if she had, he told himself. There was nothing that would tell her anything about who he really was. His fake ID was faultless. He always made sure of that.

It hadn't been touched. He knew that with a certainty born of natural instinct and years of training and experience. Everything was exactly as he'd arranged it. Every corner that was supposed to be bent was bent; every bill faced the way it was supposed to face. And the tiny bit of adhesive he'd applied to the flap that covered the ID portion of the wallet still held; she hadn't even looked to see who he was.

As straight as Linc, he thought, a vision of his old friend flashing through his mind. Although Linc had had to bend a few of his stiff principles over the years, the basic, decent and honorable core of the man had never been touched.

And you owe him, McQuade. So get the hell out of here and quit endangering the person he loves most.

"Checking to see if I stole anything before you leave?"

He spun around, then had to grab for the counter as his head whirled and grayness shadowed the edges of his vision. Damn, was he still that out of it, or was she really that quiet? The grayness retreated after a moment, allowing him an all-too-clear view of the trimly curved figure leaning against the refrigerator, clad in that vivid sweep of silky green that made her eyes glow like the gem they matched. The smooth sleekness of her hair was ruffled slightly from sleep, and the wish that his hands had done the tousling flashed through his mind before he could stop it.

Her expression was unreadable, but he knew those quick green eyes hadn't missed a thing, and her words told him she knew exactly what he'd been going to do. Despite his certainty that it had been the right idea, a feeling of guilt rose in him. It was a feeling he wasn't used to; he'd long ago had to batter that part of his conscience into insensibility or go crazy. He didn't know what to say.

"I thought about checking your wallet," she said, her tone flat. "But not for money. For something you guard much more closely. Like a clue to who you are and why you dropped into my life." She laughed, a harsh little chuckle. "At first I didn't look, because I felt embarrassed about probing into your life while you were so out of it. Can you believe that?"

His jaw tightened, and he looked away from her. He opened the wallet and pulled out a twenty. He was still going to pay her, then get the hell out of here.

"Leaving a tip?"

His gaze snapped back to her face. Her eyes flicked to the items on the counter, over the money in his hand, then back to his face. "Keep it. I'm not running a convenience store."

There was no inflection in her voice, but the words stung as if they'd been rife with sarcasm. He could read nothing in her face, but he felt the piercing gaze of those green eyes like a physical touch.

"Shiloh, I—" He lowered his eyes. "I have to get out of here," he said in a low voice, avoiding looking at her with a concentration so fierce that it made him uncomfortable.

"Don't let me stop you."

He moved to put the twenty on the counter.

"I said keep it."

"But—"

"But nothing. I don't take conscience money."

She saw too damned much, he thought, but he stuffed the bill in his pocket. "Look, I didn't want to... I mean, I didn't have any choice...." He let out a disgusted sigh at his own sudden inarticulateness. "It's just that I'm—"

"I know what you are. Or close enough. That's why I didn't bother to look in your wallet even when it became obvious you weren't going to tell me who you are. Anything I'd find in there would be fake, anyway, wouldn't it?"

He winced as her words hit home. "Shiloh—"

"Don't waste your energy denying it. I grew up with two men who've made a career out of this kind of thing. I know the signs."

"You don't understand."

"I don't? Well, let me give you my best guess, then, and you can tell me how wrong I am." She spoke evenly, as if reading things off a list. "You know Linc, well enough to find me. You get in here without leaving a trace, and you're ready to slip out the same way. Even sick, you react like a coiled rattlesnake, and judging from those scars, you've tangled with more than one of your own kind. It doesn't take a rocket scientist to figure things out."

He should have known she would guess, he thought. She was too smart not to recognize the signs, not to have picked something up from Linc through the years. Naval intelligence might be more restricted, more regimented than the free hand he usually had from his boss, but the basics were the same. He sagged wearily against the counter.

"I didn't want to come here. I tried not to." He rubbed at his eyes, which were still shadowed by dark circles of fatigue and illness. "Then I... lost track of things... and wound up here, anyway." He met her eyes then. "I'm sorry. And thank you."

"Don't thank me. Not when you're going to walk out that door and make it all for nothing." She eyed the tired slump of his body. "If you make it to the street without collapsing, it will be a miracle."

"I have to."

"So you said."

"Damn it!" he snapped, wishing she would get angry, tell him to get out, threaten to call the cops, anything except look at him so calmly and act like they were discussing the weather.

You mean anything to make her the bad guy, that little voice piped up. Butt out, he ordered it silently. "Linc would kill me if anything happened to you!"

"Probably," she agreed mildly. "He's always been very protective."

"He loves you."

"I know."

He didn't speak for a moment as a pensive, reflective look came over his face. "He told me once that you were the only thing that kept him going in that cage...."

Shiloh straightened up, only the slow care of the movement betraying any sign of the effect those quiet words had on her. For Linc to have spoken of that time to this man told her all she needed to know about how close they were, and, in turn, all she needed to know about the man who had dropped into her life.

"When he told you that, what did he call you?"

He stared at her. Was she actually asking him his name? A question at last? He was so stunned he answered her without thinking. "Con."

She considered that for a moment. "Short for?"

"Connor."

She looked at him, taking in again the thick, near black hair and the clear blue eyes. "Irish?"

"Back a ways," he answered slowly.

She nodded. "Accounts for the stubborn," she said mildly.

One dark eyebrow shot up. "Stubborn?"

She lifted one slender shoulder in an eloquent shrug. "What else would you call it? You should be flat on your back, not—" she nodded at the food on the counter "—packing to run away."

Despite her level tone the words stung. "I'm not—"

"Oh, I forgot. You have to get out of here."

"You don't understand," he said, low and harsh.

"I don't? Well, why don't you tell me where I went wrong? You're on the run, and I presume I'm supposed to believe that you're the man in the white hat. You don't want the police or any other official agency involved, so either they couldn't or wouldn't help, or you're operating too far over their lines. How am I doing so far?''

He didn't speak, but the tightness of his jaw gave her his answer.

''And whoever you're working for, something is wrong there, or you'd just have them bring you in.'' He still said nothing. ''As I said, stubborn.''

He let out a harsh breath and let his head drop back wearily. ''If you know that much, you know I can't tell you anything.''

''I don't want 'anything.' All I want to know is, did Linc send you here?''

He lifted his head and met her gaze levelly. ''You know he wouldn't. He didn't. He's . . . not involved in this. Besides, he's out of the country.''

She watched him steadily as she absorbed all the implications of what he'd said. If she'd had any doubts that he truly knew Linc, they would be gone now. Linc had left for the Middle East only three days ago, but Con already knew. So he must have tried to contact him. Even though he ''wasn't involved.''

''You really are on your own, aren't you?'' she whispered.

He let out a short, rueful chuckle. He'd never felt so alone as when he'd made himself walk away from that vision in green silk lying in the morning sun. But all he said was, ''I work better that way.''

''As long as you don't get sick.''

He couldn't deny it. ''Yeah.''

She became suddenly brisk, businesslike. ''Do you think they followed you?''

''I don't know. I was . . . pretty out of it.'' An odd look of entreaty came into his blue eyes, as if he were pleading with her to believe him. ''I really didn't mean to come here. I remember that. Telling myself not to.''

''Forget it. It doesn't matter now. What does matter is whether they know where you are.''

''I . . . don't know.''

She studied him for a moment. "You got in here even though you were too far gone to know what you were doing. I'd say it's a good bet you did whatever else you had to do, as well, including losing whoever was after you."

"I can't take that chance. I can't let you take it."

For the moment she ignored his assumption of control over her. "Look at the possibilities. One, you lost them, in which case you can only do damage by going back out there and leaving a trail for them to find. Two, you didn't lose them, and they're waiting to see what you do. I presume whoever's dogging you is not the decision maker?"

He stared at her in wonder. "Just how much did Linc tell you about this business?"

She shrugged. "Enough so I'd see it coming if it doubled back on me because of him. So, how much time do you have?"

He shook his head slowly, then let out a long breath. "I don't know. If I lost them, maybe a while, unless I left a trail they'll eventually find. If I didn't, then just until they contact their boss." His glance was an acknowledgment of the accuracy of her guess.

"They'd stay, wouldn't they? One, at least, to make sure you don't slip through their fingers?" He nodded, looking at her uneasily as he discerned some specific intent in her question. "Did you get a look at them?"

He nodded again, reluctantly. "Why?"

"So I'll know them if I find them."

"Find them?" It took a moment for her meaning to penetrate a mind still struggling to absorb how smoothly she was taking all this. He straightened up abruptly. "Oh, no. You're not going looking for them."

"Why not? They don't know me or what I look like."

"What if they saw you last night, when you got here?" Why are you even discussing this, McQuade?

"They couldn't have gotten a good look. I pulled right into the garage and closed the door before I got out."

"No."

"Look, I can even do better. There's a gate in the fence between here and my neighbor's house. I can go through it and come out of their yard on the far side. If they *are* out there, they'll never know, and I doubt if they want to call any attention to themselves by making the whole neighborhood suspicious."

"No."

She rolled her eyes in exasperation. "You've got to know—"

"You're not going out there."

"Stubborn," she muttered.

"Damn it, I'm not dragging you into this!"

"You're right, you're not. I'm in under my own steam."

"No!"

He took a swift step toward her, as if to grab her, then stopped, swaying. Sweat popped out on his forehead, and he blinked rapidly against the grayness that was back on the periphery of his vision.

"Come on." Shiloh slipped his arm over her shoulders and led him to the nearest chair in the living room. She would have tried for the bed again, but she knew he would fight her; he was trying to now. "Sit down before you fall down."

He sat. His head fell back against the cushions of the comfortably stuffed chair, and he let his eyes drift closed for a moment. He looked pale and strained, and she was suddenly determined to make sure he had the chance to get well.

She walked to her bedroom, slipped off the green robe and dressed quickly in jeans and a sweatshirt. She slid her small, narrow feet into a worn pair of deck shoes, pulled her hair up into a short, bouncy ponytail, then tugged a faded denim cap with a wide bill down over her head. She studied the effect in the mirror, then hurried to the bathroom to wash away all traces of the makeup she hadn't thought to remove last night. Then she looked again and nodded in satisfaction. For once, she thought, her freckles might come in handy.

He hadn't moved when she returned to the living room, and she thought perhaps he'd fallen asleep. But he lifted his head as she began to rustle around in the big, rolltop desk that nearly filled the one windowless wall in the room. When she'd found what she wanted and turned around, she saw his jaw drop in shock.

I know the feeling, she thought with a grin she couldn't quite keep from tugging at the corners of her mouth.

That smothered smile completed the image. "My God," he breathed. Here was the girl in the picture, all grown up. Now he could see the traces of that fourteen-year-old imp in the freshly scrubbed face, in the slender body in tight but worn jeans, her curves hidden by the loose sweatshirt. The hat was the crowning touch; she was every inch the adult version of the sassy tomboy he'd seen in that photo.

"Just sit tight and rest. I have a letter to mail." She held up the envelope she'd gotten from the desk. "There's a box two blocks down. Good excuse for a walk."

"Shiloh, please."

The "please" was much more sincere this time, although she sensed it hadn't come any easier for him.

"Don't worry. Even if they did see me last night, they won't recognize me now."

He couldn't argue with that. From what he remembered of last night, before she had donned that damned green robe, she'd been in a sleek, tailored suit, refined and chic, with her thick, auburn hair swept up into a smooth twist at the back of her head. She'd looked sophisticated and elegant, utterly unflappable, and about a million miles from the girl-next-door he was looking at now.

She could see he hadn't surrendered, and she was tired of fighting it. "I'm going," she said quietly. "Whether you tell me what to look for or I just guess is up to you."

He sat up in the chair, and she could almost see him wondering if he had the strength to stop her.

"It's only fair to warn you, I ran a pretty fair hundred-yard dash in high school."

His mouth twisted into a wry grin. "What? No black belt in karate to threaten me with?"

"Actually," she said, with a wider grin this time, one that sped up his pulse, "I was saving that. But it's judo."

Of course. It would be. Linc had been national champion. "That won't help against these guys. They're desperate."

"I got the idea you were, too," she returned softly. "Or you would never have come here."

No, he wouldn't have. If he hadn't been half out of his head with fever... He shook his head sharply, as if he could shake off the effects of that fever. God, he wished he wasn't so damned weak, too weak to stop her. He wished he'd never come here. He wished she didn't do these crazy things to him. And most of all he wished he'd never learned that wishing got you absolutely nowhere.

"Shiloh, you can't."

Her chin came up. "Oh?"

"This isn't some damned game," he snapped.

"Oh, I know that," she said in a voice gone cold. "You couldn't grow up in my family and not know that."

The memory came, but too late to call back the words. "I'm sorry. I forgot... what happened to your father. But it doesn't change anything. These guys mean business."

"And exactly what is that a professional euphemism for?"

He smiled tightly. "They ran my car off an embankment. Day before yester—no, I mean Wednesday."

Her eyebrows rose. "On the Ortega?"

He nodded, and she suppressed a shudder. She'd heard about that wreck on the news, the latest in a long line of messy crashes on the Ortega Highway that ran from the historic town of San Juan Capistrano, famous for its mission and its swallows, through the rugged Cleveland National Forest to Lake Elsinore. One car, no body. And the highway patrol had made it clear that if anyone had been in that car on that ride, it definitely would have been a body after the impact.

"You call that an embankment?" The radio had said it was a thirty-five-foot drop.

He shrugged. "I bailed out before it hit bottom."

She looked at him thoughtfully. "Then it's not something you have that they want, is it?"

"No."

"They just want you dead. Before you can do them any damage."

"Yes." He said it flatly, watching her. Her expression never changed; there was only the assessing look of someone filing away information so she would know what she was dealing with. She was incredible, he thought.

Damn, this was crazy. He shouldn't even be considering this insanity. And yet she just might be able to do it. She'd thought of a way around his every objection, and he had to admit it was a good plan. Simple, which was always the best. And Lord knows she had the cool to pull it off. God, Linc would kill him. And be right to do it.

"So are you going to tell me what I'm looking for?"

"Damn it, Shiloh," he pleaded softly, "didn't you hear what I said?"

"I heard," she said briefly. "Now, do you know if they're in the same car?"

"Why?" It burst from him involuntarily. "I've done everything you said. I broke in here, I threw you around, I've sworn at you—"

"And argued endlessly," she interrupted. "What do they look like?"

"But you don't even know me!"

She looked at him steadily for a moment before she said softly, "Tell me something, Mr.—" She stopped, realizing he'd never told her his last name.

She was about to go on without it when he unexpectedly supplied it. "—Mr. McQuade."

"Well, Mr. McQuade, if it was the other way around, if I'd come to you and given you Linc's name, what would you do?"

He sucked in a breath, and she read the answer in his eyes before he mumbled unconvincingly, "That's different."

"No. And you know it. So, are you going to help, or am I on my own?"

A look he knew had come into those green eyes, an echo of a look he'd seen in Linc's, a mix of steadfast spirit and quiet, unwavering determination. He knew then that what he'd guessed at was true; the same spun-steel core that had made Linc his one true friend in this crazy, sometimes ugly world he moved in was here as well, just less obvious beneath the beautiful and fragile-appearing exterior.

"They were in a blue sedan," he said, surrendering to that look. "A Ford, I think, full-size, four doors. I couldn't get the number, but it was a California plate. And only a rear plate. But they might have dumped it by now. It's probably kind of banged up."

"You have something to do with that?"

"I didn't exactly go over that drop voluntarily."

"Okay, scratch the car." She winced. "No pun intended."

He stared at her in awe. She was planning on going out to see if the men who had tried to kill him were waiting in ambush, and still she found humor amid the chaos.

"You are really something, Shiloh Reese."

"What I am," she said, the warmth that appeared in her eyes belying her brusque words, "is waiting. Still. So talk. What do they look like?"

Moments later, ponytail bouncing with her long, leggy strides, Shiloh disappeared out the back door to sidle through the narrow gate in the wood fence. If he'd had the strength, Con would have been pacing; as it was, he had to settle for dropping onto the sofa that faced the front windows. He could see through the lacy curtains, yet was far enough back to be invisible from the outside unless someone was standing in the front yard.

He tried to avoid the horrible images of what could be happening even now by concentrating on that yard. It was full of rich, riotous color, making the small, older, bluff-top house stand out in the crowd of similar stuccoed houses. The same way she stood out, he mused.

The yard wasn't working as a distraction, so he switched his gaze to the inside of the house, still alert for any movement from outside. The vibrant colors of the garden were echoed in the deep, jewel tones she'd used inside. She had made the house, which boasted a tiny view of the Pacific through the trees, a haven, a comfortable, cozy lair that reached out to welcome you. It was as if all the emotion she kept so battened down in herself was allowed to run free in her surroundings. He wondered if she ever let go of that unflappable control.

He swore softly at himself as an image of exactly how he would like to shake that self-possessed coolness of hers came vividly to mind. Great, McQuade. Linc would just love to read that twisted little mind of yours right now. Then, as the vision of what she'd looked like when she'd left came back to him, he felt so old and jaded it overwhelmed him. Damn, he thought defensively, thirty-four isn't exactly over the hill. It's only ten years' difference. It just felt like a hundred.

He sat there waiting, watching, for what seemed like hours. The street in front of the small house remained unhelpfully empty. Damn, he shouldn't have let her go. He should have found a way to stop her. His whole godforsaken life was coming down to an endless string of should and shouldn't haves.

If anything happened to her, Linc wouldn't have to come after him. He would jump off the nearest bridge himself. Linc was one of only two men in the world Con trusted completely, and he knew he couldn't live with the knowledge that, because of him, something had happened to Linc's beloved little sister.

Chapter 3

Con struggled to his feet, hoping that having to concentrate on staying upright would occupy his mind and help him forget how frustrated and helpless he was feeling. He walked over to the big, oak rolltop to look at the photographs he'd noticed earlier. He stopped, bracing himself with his hands on the back of the desk chair.

"What the hell?" he muttered, his eyes going rapidly from picture to picture. No, there was no doubt: the figure in each of those pictures was Shiloh. Encrusted with mud atop a powerful off-road motorcycle, plummeting earthward from a plane with only a small backpack full of parachute between her and certain death, suspended from a colorful, fragile wingspan as her hang glider soared in the sun. Jumping a long-legged horse over a wicked-looking wall, then behind the controls of a small, two-seat helicopter.

A sound at the rear of the house made him spin around. He swore as that debilitating dizziness overtook him again, and he fell back against the desk. Then she was there. "You should have stayed off your feet," she said, moving to slip his arm over her shoulders once more.

"I'm . . . all right."

"You'll be better in a minute. You're going right back to bed." She felt him tense and met his eyes. "They aren't here. There's not a car on the block that doesn't belong. And no occupied ones for four blocks in any direction. There's no one around. I even checked with Mrs. Brody, the neighborhood busybody. If she sees anything, I'll be the first to know."

"You're all right?" He looked at her as if he didn't quite believe it.

"Fine. Just a quiet Saturday morning in San Clemente. Everybody's at the beach. Now, come on."

He closed his eyes and let out a short breath. "I should go now, before they—"

"You," she cut in sharply, "are pushing stubborn over the line into stupid. Come on."

"Yes, ma'am," he said meekly, giving in. He even believed all the reasons he gave himself why: he was too sick to think straight, and out there that could get him killed; he needed time to plan, to figure out what to do; she was right—if he didn't move, he didn't leave a trail. All the reasons were true, he told himself, and ignored the little voice that was laughing in his ear.

Shiloh assented grudgingly when he said he wanted to take a shower first, and got him a towel and a razor. "Don't push it, okay? If you pass out in there, you're on your own."

"If I pass out in there, I won't care."

He didn't, but the effort cost him what little stamina he had, and he sat down on the brass bed gratefully. He could hear the muffled sounds of a washing machine and guessed that was where his clothes had disappeared to. A good thing, he thought; they needed it worse than he had.

He unknotted the towel from his waist and draped it over the footboard, then swung his feet up and grabbed the pillow to prop himself against the heavy brass uprights. He tugged the quilt and sheet over himself and stretched out, a sigh escaping him. He lay there for a moment, aware of a sweet, subtle scent surrounding him. Hers.

An odd feeling swept through him, a teasing, sensuous sensation mixed with a tinge of unease at being naked in her bed. His body quickly told him which feeling it preferred, and he shifted uncomfortably. Wonderful, McQuade, he thought sourly. You picked a great time to come out of the sexual coma you've been in. Impossible time, impossible circumstances, and, most of all, impossible woman. His body wasn't listening.

Then she came in, again carrying a tray, and still in that guise that made her look like the all-American girl-next-door. That old, tired feeling came back in a rush, doing what his mental lecturing had failed to do and cooling his body's surging heat. He'd never felt so burned out, so utterly grim about himself and his life.

"Brunch," she announced cheerfully, setting the tray on his lap and handing him a napkin. He looked at the spread of eggs, toast, fruit and orange juice and shook his head.

"You shouldn't have gone to so much work. I'll never finish it."

"Eat as much as you can. You need it if you're ever going to quit feeling like limp lettuce."

He gave her a sideways look. "That obvious, huh?"

"I've seen live people who look worse, but I can't remember when."

Suddenly, surprisingly, he grinned, and Shiloh caught her breath. Lord, he was a different person when he smiled. Those amazingly blue eyes lit up, and a pair of unexpected dimples slashed those lean cheeks. Aware that she was staring, she spoke hastily. "Go ahead and eat."

She turned and crossed to her dresser, tugging at the rubber band that held her hair while she tried not to wonder what it would be like to have those world-weary eyes light up like that not at some half-hearted joke, but for her.

He had that look, she saw now that his illness was retreating. That look her father had had, that her brother still had. That look of having seen too much of the world's ugliness, of having walked too long on the dark side. But in this man it was more; it was something her father and brother had managed to avoid. This man had lost whatever slight faith he'd ever had in his fellow human beings. It showed in the depths of those steel-blue eyes, a hundred years old in his young face.

She picked up the silver brush from the dresser and began to run it through the shining mass of her hair, restoring it to a gleaming auburn sweep of color that swung free just above her shoulders. She was lost in her own speculations about the man in her bed, unaware that, although he was eating the food she'd fixed, his eyes were glued to her reflection in the mirror.

She put down the brush and turned to face him, leaning against the edge of the dresser. He lowered his eyes and concentrated on eating.

"Con?"

He nearly jumped, so startling was the sound of his name in that low, lovely voice. He covered it with a cough and reached for the orange juice. "What?" he managed to get out as he set the glass back down after a long swallow.

"When did you last see Linc?"

He thought for a moment. "Last year, after he got back from . . . his last assignment."

She sighed impatiently. "I know, the Persian Gulf. You haven't seen him since?"

"No. I've been . . . busy."

"I wanted to see him before he had to leave again, but they wouldn't give him any time."

"That's the military for you. Ship you around like you were a piece of furniture."

She looked at him quizzically. "You're not . . . ?"

"One of their pieces? No. I'm strictly private. I find corporate security a bit less . . . cramped. Less spit and polish."

"And rules?"

He lifted a shoulder in a one-sided shrug, but a brief flash of that crooked grin gave her her answer.

Her mouth quirked; then her delicately arched brows furrowed. "Then how did you ever meet my brother?"

He took another swallow of orange juice as he considered what to say. He supposed it couldn't hurt to tell her; it had nothing to do with this mess.

''Our paths crossed on something a few years ago. He was working on it for the navy, I was on the private side. We kept running into each other, getting in each other's way. So we decided to work together, mainly to keep from killing each other.'' The grin flashed again, no less devastating than before. ''He's all right—for a military type.''

She'd been watching him intently as he spoke, comprehension dawning in the green eyes. ''In the Philippines?''

He stared at her. ''What?''

''He told me. When he came back. Oh, not about the case, he never talks about those, but that he'd met some guy he'd thought was going to be a real problem but who turned out to be the best man he'd ever worked with.''

''Linc said that?''

''Yes.'' She was warmed by his look of pleasure at her brother's compliment. Not all of that faith had been lost, it seemed. She walked to the lounge she'd pulled up next to the bed and sat. ''He said he'd even tried to recruit you. Said if he could get you, he could get rid of half of his staff.''

''As I recall, he said most of them were bumbling idiots,'' he said with a crooked grin that made her throat go tight again.

''That's my brother. Wild and free with the praise.''

''I thought he was. About you, anyway. I was wrong.''

She blushed when his meaning hit her. ''He's . . . prejudiced. All big brothers are, you know.''

''You're very close, aren't you?''

''Yes, I suppose so, considering there're fifteen years between us. Or maybe because of it. My father...'' She trailed off, unable to finish the sentence. She looked up to meet a pair of blue eyes warm with sympathy and understanding. How had she ever thought those eyes cold? ''I think we're closer because of what happened to Daddy. He's very good to me, even though he's a little overprotective at times.''

Yeah, he muttered to himself. Remember that, McQuade, and keep your evil thoughts to yourself. ''Your father . . . how is he now?''

''Better. He gets around okay on crutches, but it tires him, so he still uses the wheelchair most of the time.''

"And mentally?"

He saw the old, familiar worry in her face, as he had often seen it in Linc's. "About the same, I think he would have been all right if it hadn't been for what happened to Linc. I was only five when we got the news, but I remember. It really set him back. He knew, all the time the Vietcong were holding him, what he was going through. He could take it himself, but his son . . ."

She shrugged. "It comes and goes. He's fine for weeks, even months. Then, in his mind, he's gone for a while. To wherever he had to go to survive what they did to him."

"Sometimes it's all you can do." Con's voice sounded oddly distant. "You send your mind away to where it doesn't matter what happens to your body anymore."

He came back to himself abruptly, but she had seen the memories in his eyes, dark and haunting. She forced herself not to look at the thin, white scar curving down from his shoulder.

"Daddy's doing fine now, though. He's working on a book he's been writing for years, on his hobby."

"The Civil War?"

Shiloh looked at him ruefully. "You know about that, huh?"

He chuckled, and, like the grin, it was unexpected. It made her throat tighten and her heart pound.

"How could I not?" he said, still smiling. "Shiloh and Lincoln Reese? To borrow a phrase, it doesn't take a rocket scientist to figure out somebody has a thing for that part of history."

"I was lucky I didn't end up Gettysburg."

"Or Appomattox."

She giggled, and Con thought he would do just about anything to keep hearing that lovely, silvery sound. So he did. He talked to her, asked her questions, got her talking about the good memories. He had developed a knack for drawing people out over the years; he had rather glumly put it down to being something of a vacuum himself.

Whatever the reason, it had come in handy more than once, netting him some very useful pieces of information.

He just listened, skimming along the surface and picking out what he needed. Using the human foible of being one's own favorite topic of conversation to his advantage. Just using. And not letting himself think about when he had come to look on people as tools to be used to get the job done.

But he was aware of the difference now. He was engrossed in everything she told him while at the same time aware of how odd it felt just to listen to someone, with no thought of gleaning information from them, no need to pry that one essential slip or name or place from them. He just listened. And enjoyed.

It didn't take him long to realize her favorite topic of conversation was not herself but her brother. At first he'd thought it was because of his connection with Linc, but after a while it became obvious that she truly adored her older brother.

"I was eight when he finally came home. He was still pretty sick, and he was laid up for a long time. He always seemed to want me around, and I was very—" she laughed "—proud of that. I understood it later, that he just needed to see a child who hadn't been hurt, an...innocent face that hadn't seen the horror, that hadn't had to live with the terror."

"It was more than that," Con put in. "He told me that when things got bad he kept telling himself that he had to hang on, had to survive to get back. 'I wanted to see what kind of woman that little scamp would turn into,' he said. Now I know why."

Shiloh blushed. Lord, when was the last time he'd seen a woman who blushed at simple compliments? And changed the subject as if she were afraid more might be coming?

"You'd better get some rest if you're going to beat this thing."

He didn't want to sleep. He wanted her to keep talking; he wanted to listen to that lovely low voice; he wanted to know everything about her, and she hadn't even begun to talk about herself.

Dangerous ground, McQuade, he warned himself. As soon as you're strong enough, you're gone, so back off. Don't get in too deep.

So he did as she said, trying to stifle the tiny voice that told him he was much too late with his own warning.

He awoke briefly in the evening, surprised that he had slept so long, but feeling much better. She brought him a dinner of steak and steamed vegetables that tasted like heaven, even eaten between apologies for putting her to so much work.

"Shut up and eat," she said, not at all sharply. He shut up and ate.

Shiloh cleaned up the dishes, then went back into the bedroom. He was already asleep again, which pleased her. He was looking much better; that hollow look was gone, and the shadows beneath his eyes were fading. He might be doing pretty well by tomorrow, now that he'd had some rest and some decent food.

And what would he do then? Drop out of her life as quickly as he had dropped in? Without a trace? She knew that was what he intended, knew it as surely as if she'd known him for years instead of since—Lord, was it only yesterday?

She sat back on the lounge, stretching out her long legs on the rich, green-and-ruby-patterned cushion. He looked so different asleep, she thought, so much younger. And he had seemed that way this afternoon, when he had somehow gotten her talking in a way that was totally unlike her. Just as Linc had always been able to do. Trick of the trade, she supposed, resolutely smothering the half-formed wish that he had been truly interested.

If only she could reach Linc. She had long ago become resigned to his being out of touch for long periods, and although nothing could ease her worry about him, she tried her best to keep it under control. She refused to add to his concerns by falling apart every time he left; he'd had too much of that, as had her father. But now, for the first time in a long time, she wished for a way to get through to him. If anybody could help Con, he could. He would find a way.

She didn't even wonder at her willingness to accept Con as being in the right in this situation, whatever it was. Linc had always told her that she had good instincts about people and to trust them; she was trusting them now.

Watching Con as he slept, she had time to remember what her beloved brother had said that day when he'd come back from the Philippines.

"He's a loner, Shy, but I think it's because he's never known anything else. He doesn't have any family, and I get the feeling it's been that way for a long time. But I'll tell you, little one, I've never met anybody I'd rather have on my side. Or anybody I'd want to go up against less."

And then, there in the darkness, she remembered what else Linc had said. She had, in trying to stop herself from worrying about him, put it out of her mind until now. But there it was, as clearly as if he were sitting beside her as he had that day, his long, rugged face drawn into harsh lines as he looked at her, not speaking.

"I'm not a little girl anymore," she had told him, seeing the doubt in his eyes even as she sensed his need to talk.

"No," he'd said, his hazel eyes warm with that light they always held for her. "You're not."

"Then talk to me." Still he'd hesitated. "It's that bad? It must be, or you'd just talk to Dad. So it must be something that would make him worry. It got messy?"

Linc had let out a wry chuckle. "I forgot how sharp you are. Yes, it got messy." That was when he had looked at her and said quietly, "He took a bullet for me, Shy. I would have been dead."

Would have been dead. Her beloved brother in a flag-draped casket, with some naval officer speaking meaningless words. And he would have been followed by her father. She had no doubt that his fragile health would not have withstood that blow. Both of them, gone, but for this man. She looked at him with eyes stinging with tears.

Which of those scars had Linc's name on it? And why hadn't he told her? Even when he had finally used Linc's name, he hadn't told her, hadn't played the one card that would have assured him of her cooperation. Why? She pondered the question for a long time before sleep claimed her.

Con came awake abruptly, every nerve taut, every sense tingling. He lay carefully still, listening. Nothing. He inched his head to the side just far enough to see that Shiloh was still asleep, curled on the wicker lounge. He held his breath, his ears straining for any sound.

Still nothing. But something had brought him awake, and he had lived too long by trusting that ingrained instinct to ignore it now. Moving with exquisite slowness, he edged the covers back and sat up. Then he stopped again, waiting. The silence stayed unbroken, but that sixth sense was screaming. He stood up.

Moving with a silent, light-footed grace that was surprising for a man his size, he crossed to the doorway to the living room. He paused with his back to the wall, his head turned to catch any sound from the other room. He tried to make himself forget the innocently sleeping woman and concentrate on the silence, but an image of her getting hurt—or worse—because of him just wouldn't go away.

Then he heard it, the slightest of sounds, a mere whisper of cloth against cloth. From inside the house. They were here. There was no time for recriminations, for wishing he hadn't stayed. Every bit of his strength, every ounce of determination, everything he'd ever learned about survival, was now channeled toward one goal: the safety of Shiloh Reese.

He searched the dim room for something, anything, within reach. He saw a reflection on the dresser and realized it was the ornate silver comb that matched the brush she had used. It was long, narrow, with a handle that came to a point at the end. He just managed to reach it, gauging the length of it, the sharpness of that point. It might be enough. He heard the sound again, closer.

He forced himself to breathe shallowly. How many? There had been two on his tail since WestAir. And two in the car that had run him off the road. Still two? And how the hell had they found him so fast? Three days. They were good. Too damned good.

The sound came again, and this time he saw the shadow. He crouched, waiting, knowing he would have to move fast. If she woke up before he got it done . . .

Suddenly the shadow filled the doorway, and he lunged, thrusting upward with the makeshift dagger. He heard a startled cry, then a grunt as the weapon caught and skidded upward. The heavy body reeled backward into the living room. Con went with it, using his weight to bear it down to the floor, hearing the thud of impact as the man hit the coffee table.

He sensed the sudden movement behind him and rolled off the now limp man beneath him, dodging the hulking shape that was bearing down on him. The room was dark, but there was enough light to outline the unmistakable shape of the pistol in the man's hand. No silencer, Con's mind registered. In that split second he moved. Lying on his back, he brought his knees up, then drove his feet straight into the midsection of that considerable target, gambling that the man would only fire the weapon, rousing the neighborhood, as a last resort.

He heard the whoosh of air leaving the man's lungs as Con's bare feet dug into his solar plexus. Con rolled upward, letting the man's own momentum carry him up and over to crash to the floor. Twisting his body swiftly sideways, Con came to his knees, straining to see in the near blackness of the room. The barest of movements alerted him, the slightest of glints as what light there was found the barrel of the revolver as it moved, lifted.

He dived, coming down hard on the sprawled attacker, his hand clamping around the wrist of the hand that held the gun. He forced it to the floor over the man's head, then had to twist violently sideways to avoid the wicked blow of a serge-clad knee as it aimed for his vulnerable nakedness.

His evasive move gave the burly man the leverage he needed. He came up off the floor in a rush of snarling anger. He spat a vicious epithet, then brought the barrel of the gun down in a smashing blow. Only Con's hair-trigger reflexes saved him from a crushed skull.

The blow glanced off his temple, stunning him for a moment. He felt a hard, merciless pressure on his throat, digging, throttling, and he knew he was in trouble. He felt the hammer of the gun gouging into the side of his neck as the man crouched over him, one massive knee driving into his chest, forcing out what little air he had. The four inch barrel was across his throat, compressing his windpipe and cutting his air down to a bare trickle.

He bucked beneath the killing weight as his ears began to ring and flashes of light shot across his field of vision. He couldn't budge the smothering bulk and cursed his own weakness. He felt the world begin to spin away.

Over the growing hum in his ears he heard the familiar sound of the slide of a .45 automatic being worked, chambering a round. There had been a third man, he thought numbly. A third man he hadn't seen or counted on. He'd blown this from square one and gotten himself killed doing it. And maybe Shiloh. God, no...

"Back off."

Con blinked. He must be hallucinating, closer to death than he'd thought. He must be, because he'd just heard Shiloh's voice, low and husky and deadly calm. The pressure on his throat lifted, and he felt the sudden tensing in the body still straddling him.

"Don't."

Con was gasping for breath, fighting to understand. The ringing in his ears ebbed, and the flashing lights faded. Gradually his vision cleared, and he saw that the .45 he'd heard was there all right, but instead of being aimed at him, it was pressed with deadly intent just behind the right ear of the man atop him. And it was held in a hand that was rock steady for all its delicate slenderness.

Shiloh.

His breath stopped in his battered throat. It was breath he couldn't afford to lose, and he had to gulp it in as things began to whirl again.

"Reverse the gun. Hand it over, butt first."

The burly man obeyed and Shiloh backed up a step. "Put your hands on your head and get off him."

His eyes trained uneasily on the chrome-finished pistol, he obeyed. Shiloh reached over and flipped on the lamp beside the couch, tilting the shade so that no sudden flare of light would blind her or Con and give the man now on his knees a chance.

Slowly, one hand rubbing at his throat, Con sat up. He was torn between staring at her in shock and keeping a wary eye on the man who had come a hair's breadth away from killing him.

When Shiloh saw that Con was fairly steady once more, she tossed him the gun that had nearly choked the life out of him. Automatically he checked the load, then leveled it on the huge man who was sitting rather awkwardly back on his heels, eyeing Con angrily and Shiloh with nothing short of astonishment.

Con waited. He let the life pulse back through him, waiting for the relief to subside. He had to think now, not about what she had done, but about finding out what he needed to know from this man. He swallowed, wondering if he would be able to talk.

The ham-fisted man shifted uncomfortably, and without a word Con thumbed the hammer back on the revolver, cocking it. The man froze. Only then did Shiloh lower the automatic, although she didn't set it down. Instead, she sat on the edge of the coffee table, watching Con. She saw the change come over him, the speed with which he regained control. She saw his breathing even out, his hand leave his bruised throat, his muscles tense slightly, as if awaiting any hint of movement from the man before him.

And she saw the cold come back into those blue eyes, chilling them to an iceberg hue. This was the man who had stared down at her in those first seconds after he had pinned her to the bed, the eyes that had sent a shiver rippling down her spine.

With an effort Shiloh controlled the shudder that wanted to break loose. She would not fall apart now, she told herself severely.

"Is he dead?" she asked, nodding toward the other man, collapsed near the doorway to the bedroom. As if in answer, a low moan rose from the huddled shape.

"I guess not," Con said, his voice raspy but strong enough. "But that can be remedied."

On the surface, Shiloh never blinked; inside, her stomach knotted. Would he really do it? Killing a man in a fight was one thing, but afterward, when the immediate danger was past? It's his job, she reminded herself. Just like it was Linc's job. But would her brother so cold-bloodedly murder an already helpless man?

"For both of them," Con added harshly, his eyes fastened on the man whose muscles were beginning to tremble with the effort of maintaining his awkward position.

"You wouldn't dare," the man spat out. "You can't afford the cops asking—"

"Why I shot a burglar? And an armed one at that?" Con smiled, a chilling curve of his lips that matched the icy blue of his eyes. "We caught you in the act, for all the police need to know. As long as our side of the story is the only one that gets told . . ." He saw fear flash for a moment in the flat, muddy brown eyes.

"I am a little curious, though," he said in a deceptively casual tone, "about how you found me so fast. Maybe even curious enough to let you live long enough to tell me."

The man swore, low and ugly; Con shrugged and shifted the hand that held the gun, his finger visibly tightening.

"All right, damn it! Ease off that thing. It's got a touchy trigger."

Con tilted the weapon slightly, one eyebrow raised in interest as he inspected it. "Oh? How touchy?" he asked, giving every indication as he leveled it again that he was about to find out for himself.

"Too touchy!" the man yelped, then rushed on. "Look, they just gave us this address, told us to check it out. That's all I know!" Con eased the hammer down, looking at the man reflectively, not at all as if the words had been another hammer blow to his aching gut.

Shiloh had been watching with a rather grim interest, but the man's words made her stomach knot again. They'd been given her address?

"When?" Con snapped out.

"This afternoon. We'd been on ice ever since the boss found out you weren't in that car." A touch of confusion came over the heavy, broken-nosed face. "How'd you pull that off?"

Con ignored him. "When are you supposed to report back?"

"As soon as you're..." The man stopped, eyeing the deadly little tunnel of the gun's barrel, then added hastily, "Or by daylight, if something went wrong."

For a split second Con's eyes flicked to Shiloh, the blue depths holding a silent tribute to the fact that she had been that something.

"What else did he tell you?"

"Nothing. Just that you might be here." The man glanced at Shiloh, a leering smile pulling at his pudgy mouth, then looked back at Con. "I'll give you one thing, Miller—no, it's McQuade, isn't it?—you've got taste. Is she any good?"

"Another crack like that and you won't like what you'll be tasting," Con bit out, aware of the sudden color that had risen to Shiloh's cheeks at the man's insinuation.

Shiloh felt it too, that unaccustomed flush that heated her cheeks again, but unlike Con, she knew the real cause. Until now she had been so wrapped up in the tension, the drama of what was unfolding so unexpectedly in her living room, that she hadn't really focused on the rather obvious fact that the man now holding the gun on the unwanted guest in her house was stark naked.

It wasn't the bulky intruder's innuendo that had caused her blush; it was the realization that she had, on some level, been aware of Con's nudity since the moment she had stepped into the room. In the dim light it had been the flash of bare skin and taut, flexing muscles as he had tried to fight off the man who outweighed him by a good fifty pounds; now, in the lamplight, it was the sculptured perfection of his leanly muscled body, the scars that marked the sleek skin somehow only emphasizing the beauty of it.

Oh, yes, she had been very aware of it, and that awareness sent her blood racing through her veins in a way she didn't understand. She felt a little tremor go through her, and she bit the inside of her lip to control it. Control. She'd worked at it all her life, had thought she'd mastered it, but now she wasn't so sure. She tried again; and was rewarded with a steady tone when she spoke.

"Now what?"

Con shrugged. "Don't need him anymore. Just them showing up here tells me what I needed to know." He cocked the gun again; the man paled.

"Hey, take it easy! I was just doin' what I was told, you know?"

"I know." He leveled the gun once more.

"Look, maybe we can make a deal, okay?" Desperation lit the muddy brown eyes. "I know some things, some people."

"I told you, you already proved what I needed to know. I was right about your boss, or he wouldn't be so eager to get rid of me before I can blow the whistle on him."

"But you don't have any proof. How can you turn him in without proof?"

"What makes you think I intend to turn him in?" Con's deceptively calm tone completed the freeze in his eyes and that cold smile had begun. Shiloh felt as if she were looking at someone she'd never seen before.

"You . . . have to. You're FBI, aren't you? Like that guy we had to—" He broke off, going white as he realized what he'd said.

"Thanks," Con said with that awful smile. "You just iced the cake for me. I never believed that accident story. His boss will be very interested to hear that."

"His boss? You mean you're not—"

"FBI? No. Or from any other government agency that has its hands tied by rules and regulations. And your boss is going to find that out."

The beefy man let out a low whistle. "You're crazy, man! You'll never get close to him again. He knows you were a plant, and he'll never stop coming after you."

An oddly speculative light came into Con's frosty blue eyes. That chilling, terrible smile widened. "You just bought your miserable life, Moose. Because you're going to go back to that crooked, murdering boss of yours and tell him to come on ahead. I'll be waiting."

"What?" The man gaped at him.

"I'd much rather deal with him myself. My boss has a tendency to be too... civilized." He lowered the gun, easing down the hammer once more.

Shiloh let out a breath she hadn't been aware of holding. At least she wasn't going to have a bloodbath in her living room. Con lifted his head to look at her, and the thaw she saw when those blue eyes met hers amazed her.

"Can you find something to tie this clown up with?"

"Wait a minute!" Moose squeaked. "I thought you said—"

"Shut up." He didn't even glance at the man, who immediately shut up.

Shiloh studied him for a long moment; then, with a nod, she got up. She went to a closet, digging in a large box until she found an old length of nylon line and went back to the living room. She handed it to him wordlessly. She watched as he tied the man up securely, over his whining protests. Now that he was assured of living, Moose's fear had degenerated into shameless begging. With a gesture of irritation, Con grabbed for one huge shoe and yanked it off the man's foot.

"As they say, put a sock in it," he said, and did so.

Shiloh had to stifle a giggle. Great, she told herself accusingly, you've fallen into the middle of mayhem. You've got one man trussed up like a Thanksgiving turkey, another probably bleeding to death all over your floor, and a third running around wearing a gun and nothing else....

"I'll check on his partner," she said abruptly.

"I'll do it." Con didn't think he'd hurt the man badly, but he didn't want her to be the one to find out if he had.

"I'll do it! Just go put something on, will you?"

To her surprise no more than his own, he blushed. "I . . . I'm sorry."

He turned away from her with a jerky little movement, reddening furiously now. He didn't understand it. He'd never been so aware of his own nudity, not since... Not since he'd slid naked into her bed.

Shiloh couldn't quite believe what she was seeing. Was this the same Connor McQuade she had just seen turn Moose into a squeaking mouse with only an icy stare? Right now he looked totally disconcerted, and, at odds with that solid, completely adult male body, his expression was that of an embarrassed ten-year-old boy.

"It's not that I don't like the view," she teased, "but you are a bit . . . distracting."

His head came up then, his eyes searching her face with an intensity she didn't understand. She met his look questioningly, and he seemed to relax, as if letting out a tensely held breath. With a short, jerky nod that could have meant anything, he got up and strode into the bedroom.

Shiloh forced herself not to look. It didn't help. She could see the long, muscled legs, the bunching and flexing of his taut buttocks, as if she had watched every lithe stride. It had done her just as little good to look away when he had first gotten out from under Moose's weight. She felt as if she already knew that wide, muscled chest by heart, and hadn't been able to keep her gaze from slipping down that sleek smoothness to the intriguing, narrow path of dark hair that began at his navel and plunged downward to widen into thick curls at the base of his flat belly and beyond.

She felt her color rise again as her imagination dropped those last strategic inches, supplying all the details with vivid clarity. Good grief, she chastised herself, you're acting like you've never seen a naked man before. Get to work here. She turned back to the man on the floor.

Chapter 4

Keeping the .45 close just in case, she knelt beside the moaning man and nudged him over onto his back. His lip and one eye were red and swollen, and he was clutching his right side. He looked up at her, eyes unfocused.

"Bastard stabbed me," he muttered.

Her brow furrowed. It didn't look like a stab wound; it was more of a long, deep scratch that had bled only a little. Besides, where would Con have gotten a knife in time to—

Her thoughts broke off as a silver glint from the floor caught her eye. She reached for it, then stared in shock. Disbelief gave way to amazement, then to rising laughter.

Then Con was there, kneeling down to look at her a little warily, as if thinking her calm had at last dissolved into hysteria. She held up the narrow silver comb.

"You went after two of them with this?"

He shrugged, then grinned a little crookedly. "It was the best I could do at the time. My gun was in the car."

A flash as bright and fleeting as the glint off the silver in her hand came and went in her vivid green eyes. It was admiration, and it warmed him to the core in a way he had never known.

The man on the floor moaned again.

"Oh, be quiet," Shiloh said unsympathetically. "You're barely scratched."

"I've been stabbed!"

"You've been combed, you idiot!" She looked at Con to ask if they were going to tie up Mr. Tough Guy, but stopped at the look on his face. "What?"

"I...you're..." He shook his head, at a loss. "Any more of that line left?"

She got it, and when they had Moose's whining compatriot equally immobilized and tucked away in a corner, she sat back on her heels and with quick, sure movements ejected the round she'd chambered into the .45, returned it to the clip and put the safety back on. Con watched every move. He didn't speak until she was done, his words soft, so they couldn't be overheard.

"Why didn't you pull that on me first thing?"

"It seemed like overkill," she said with a shrug, in the same quiet voice. "You were already too sick to do much." She got up and crossed to the desk, out of earshot of the two men, and set the weapon down. Con had followed her, smiling wryly.

"Just how good are you with that?"

"Adequate." His eyebrows went up. "Okay," she admitted. "Maybe a little better than adequate."

"Who taught you?" he asked, thinking he knew the answer.

"My father." She caught his look of surprise. "Just like he taught my brother. His legs may be crippled, but he can still center-punch an ace at fifty yards."

The love and pride in her voice made his throat tighten. He'd never minded not having that kind of feeling in his life. At least, he hadn't thought so. Linc had made him wonder what it would have been like; Linc's sister made him feel the enormity of what he had missed.

"Linc gave me the .45 for my eighteenth birthday."

She had a quiet, reflective look in her eyes, and Con was seized with a wish to have known her then, and at the fourteen in Linc's picture, and at every age before and after, a wish so fierce it left him unable to speak.

He leaned back against the desk. She made him wish for too damned much, made him wish for things he could never have, would never have.

"Are you all right?" She was looking at him with a concern that did nothing to halt those wishes.

"Yeah. Thanks to you." He turned to look at her. "Shiloh, I—"

"Later. What are we going to do with Tweedledum and Tweedledumber there?"

A grin sent those unexpected dimples flashing again. "You never give in to it, do you?"

"Not if I can help it."

Her voice held an undertone of vehemence that surprised him. Then it was gone as, after looking at him for a moment, she said softly, "There really isn't anyone you can call or go to?"

His jaw went rigid. "Don't think I haven't been wishing there was. Hell, I'd call Linc, if there was a prayer of getting through to him. But there isn't. And my boss is out of the country. Even if I could reach him, there isn't time."

After a moment she nodded. He wondered what she thought of a man whose list of friends he could turn to with trust was so very short. But she only repeated her question about what to do with the two would-be assassins.

"I hate having garbage lying around," he said. "I'll go find their car and load them up."

Something in his tone warned her. "And then?"

There was a long moment of silence before, his voice low and full of reluctance, he spoke again. "They know where you live." She waited. His eyes came up to meet hers. "They'll know you helped me. They'll probably think you were in on it all along."

"And that's what they'll tell their boss, if you let them go."

He nodded. "I'm sorry, Shiloh, but I can't call the police, either. Not yet."

"And when they talk to their boss…" His silence was her answer. She glanced at the two men tied up in her dining room alcove. Then her chin came up, and she looked at Con levelly. "Do I have time to pack?"

His eyes widened, and the knot of apprehension that had been building in him at the thought of having to force her to leave her home vanished. Cool under fire, he thought, just like her brother.

"Must be in the blood," he muttered.

"I hope so," she said, that same oddly fervent note in her voice. "I hope I got some of the good side along with the bad." He looked at her quizzically. "Never mind," she said quickly. "How much time do I have?"

"Not much," he said. "Those two not withstanding, these guys are good." He looked thoughtful. "Maybe we can buy some time, though." His tone became crisp, commanding. "Pack what you need, but keep it light. As fast as you can. Don't forget a jacket, or something warm. Throw together whatever food you've got that's simple, ready to go."

"Yes, sir." Shiloh snapped off a smart, military salute.

Con had the grace to look sheepish. "Sorry. Force of habit." He let out a breath. "Look, I don't know when or where we'll be able to stop. Or even if we will, if they—" He stopped as her expression registered.

"I'm going…with you?"

He looked perplexed. "What did you think?"

"Just that you wanted me out of here. I figured I was on my own after that."

"Is that what you think of me? That I'd leave you to deal with this alone?" He was surprised at how much it stung.

"No." She was a little confused by the look of pain in his face. "I…you have a job to do. I'd just be in the way."

He stared at her. "You really do know this business, don't you?"

"I cut my teeth on it," she said simply. "So don't worry about me. I'll be fine. I'll just—"

"You'll just nothing," he cut in. "I got you into this, and I'll see that you get out of it. In one piece."

"And get the job done at the same time? Isn't that spreading yourself a little thin?" He only shrugged. "Look, they want *you*. They won't bother me—"

"You're damned right they won't." His jaw was rigid.

"Stubborn," she murmured, barely audible.

"Look," he said, grabbing her arms to turn her to face him. "It's my fault they came here. You could have gotten hurt, or worse. I'm not taking any more chances on them getting a shot at you."

"You're going to have enough to do just to stay alive yourself, without me along. You don't have to protect me."

An odd gleam came into his clear blue eyes. "Maybe I need you to protect me. You did a hell of a job tonight."

Shiloh flushed, pleased at his praise, but stuck to her guns. "Then you know I'll be fine. Just take care of yourself." He didn't move. "Go on."

"No."

"Why?" she asked impatiently, not understanding why he was being so obstinate about it. He had to see that it was for the best.

He didn't understand it himself. He only knew that he could no more walk away and leave her to the winds of fate than he could fly. No matter what common sense told him, no matter how high the odds were that she was right, no matter how clearly she had just shown him that she was no helpless female, he couldn't turn away. He had neither the time nor the nerve to analyze why, so he turned to the only reason that made any sense to him.

"I can't let anything happen to you. I owe it to your brother."

She felt an odd sensation that, absurdly, seemed almost like disappointment. Then his words penetrated.

"I got the idea that he owed you." He looked at her questioningly. "Which scar is it?" she asked softly. "The one you took for him?"

Con stared, startled. "You . . . know about that?"

She nodded slowly. "I didn't put it together until last night. That you were the one, I mean. He told me you took a bullet that was meant for him."

He lowered his eyes, his fingers going in a reflexive motion to the scar at his hairline. "Did he also tell you that he carried me out of there?" Shiloh went suddenly still.

"No, he wouldn't, would he?" he said softly. "I was out the whole time. One hundred ninety-five pounds of dead weight, and he carried me over a mile to the jeep. Got me to the navy hospital." He dropped his hand from the scar. "I owe him, all right."

Shiloh thought she heard him add, "And for more than that," but the words were so low she wasn't sure.

Con came out of his reverie to find her watching him intently. He let out a long breath, wondering what would convince her that she had to come with him for her own good. When she spoke, it was to ask the last thing he expected.

"Why didn't you tell me?"

"What?"

"You were going to leave, as sick as you were . . . but all you had to do was tell me who you were, what you did for Linc. Why didn't you?"

"I told you. I didn't want to come here in the first place. I never meant to drag you into this."

"I know. But you were already here."

"Yeah." His voice was tired, dull. "I don't even know how. I don't remember much, after the crash."

"Con—"

"Let's get going. Only about three hours until dawn. We don't have time to waste. When the boss doesn't hear from them, he'll send reinforcements."

He expected a protest, but she merely gave him a look that told him she was only postponing the rest of the conversation, then disappeared into the bedroom.

Well, he thought as he took the keys he'd found in Moose's pocket and went out to search for his car, you wanted her to ask questions. You should have known she wouldn't ask the ones you expected.

Two blocks away he found a near twin to the car that had run him over the cliff and wasn't surprised when the key fit. He got in and drove it up to the house.

When he went back inside, he heard her in the kitchen. He noted with some surprise that there were already a small nylon suitcase and a large canvas bag on the floor of the living room, then wondered why he was surprised.

When he walked into the kitchen he saw she already had several things out on the counter. She looked up from where she was kneeling in front of a cupboard.

"You found their car?" He nodded. "Are we taking it?"

"Yes. But we'll take yours, too. I want to dump theirs somewhere. It might throw them off."

Shiloh nodded, relieved. She somehow didn't relish the idea of riding in the same car with those two. "I'll load this up, then." She reached for one of the bags she'd filled.

"Leave it. I'll do it after I get them in the car."

"Are you going to . . . dump them with it?"

"No." He smiled crookedly. "I'm going to check our guests into a motel, with orders not to be disturbed. With any luck, nobody will find them for a couple of days."

"You're going to leave them tied up?"

He let out a short breath. "Have to. It's the only way to buy us some time. I know it sounds—"

"—like less than they deserve," she cut in smoothly. "They came here to commit murder, didn't they?" And it would be a long, long time, Shiloh thought, before she would forget the image of Con going up against those two thugs and their guns armed with only a comb.

She followed him out to the living room and watched while he hauled Moose to his feet.

"Where are *we* going?" she asked, looking thoughtful.

"I don't know yet."

"Well, I was thinking, I know this beach house down in San Diego—"

"Later!" he snapped, cutting her off, then regretted his tone. She'd been so calmly efficient that he'd begun to forget she wasn't a pro at this.

When he had his two unwilling passengers stuffed into the back seat, still chewing on their own socks, he came back and helped her pack up the rest of the food. Setting aside the first full bag, he looked at her.

"Any other weapons in the house?"

"No."

"Bring the .45, then. I'll take theirs."

She merely nodded. He sighed, searching for words. "I'm sorry I jumped on you. I didn't want to talk in front of them." He gave her a conciliatory smile. "What house?"

She paused, humor glinting in her green eyes as she looked at him. "There isn't one."

"What?" He looked blank.

"There isn't one. I just said that for them."

Con stared at her, mouth open. A chuckle broke from him, and then he was laughing, full-blown, roaring laughter, as he hadn't let loose in more years than he could remember.

Shiloh grinned, a little lopsidedly. Lord, he had a wonderful laugh, even if it did sound a little rough, as if it had been stored away unused for a long time. She guessed it had been; not much remembered joy shone in those blue eyes.

"I will never," he promised, "underestimate you again, Ms. Reese."

If he was surprised that her car was in fact a bright red four-wheel-drive Blazer, it didn't show in his face as he loaded the food while she tossed her bags in the back. He turned to look at her.

"I didn't mean you had to travel that light," he said; based on the glamorous woman who had come home that night, he'd expected twice as much luggage.

"I've got all I need."

"I don't know how long this is going to take before it's . . . okay for you to come back."

"Safe, you mean? You don't have to sugarcoat it for me. I've had escape plans drilled into my head ever since I was old enough to understand, in case something went sour in my father's work, then my brother's." She stopped, the first sign of worry he'd seen coming into her eyes. "Con . . ."

"What?"

"My father . . ."

She didn't have to explain. "Where is he?"

"Santa Barbara. He's still in our house there."

"He should be fine. Like you said, they're after me."

"But they knew you might be at my house."

"Yes."

She studied his expression. "And you know how they knew."

It wasn't a question. He sucked in a breath, his lips thinning out as his jaw tightened.

"I don't know how they knew, but I have a good idea who told them. The same guy who's had somebody on my tail since the beginning." He tossed a box of food in the back of the Blazer with considerably more force than necessary. "I just don't know who's running him," he muttered.

He slammed the back loading door shut, then looked at her. "Your father will be all right. For a while, at least. They're going to be looking for me and trying to figure out just where you come in." She looked at him silently. "It's the lesser of two evils, Shiloh," he said tautly. "If you go off by yourself, they just might think you had nothing to do with it. But it's doubtful, and you'd be too damn vulnerable alone. Besides, they'd probably grab you, anyway...."

"To get to you?" He nodded. She wanted, ridiculously, to ask if it would work. She didn't.

"As soon as I can, I'll get someone to your father's place to make sure nothing happens. I just need a little time to sort things out."

"To figure out who the black hats are?"

He didn't deny it. "There's a joker in the deck somewhere. I just don't know where yet. And until I do..."

"We're on our own."

"Yes."

"In what?"

He blinked at her.

"In what, exactly, are we on our own?"

"Shiloh, I can't."

"You mean you won't."

He sighed. "If you like."

She studied him for a long moment. "You still don't trust me."

The words were flat, emotionless, but Connor didn't miss the pain hidden beneath them. He couldn't stand it, and the words broke from him.

"I'd trust you with my life."

"But not the truth."

"Shi—"

"Never mind. What I don't know can't get me in trouble, right? I recognize the protective streak. My brother has one a mile wide, just like my father." Her voice was cool when she went on. "We'd better get going." She walked to the driver's door. "Am I following you?"

After the moment it took him to absorb the change in her, Con said, "No. I don't know how good a look they got at this—" he jerked a thumb toward the Blazer "—but there's no sense giving them a second chance. There's a motel just off the freeway in Oceanside. I'll drop them there. Maybe it will add some more punch to your little diversion about San Diego." He spared a brief second to flash her a smile of salute. "Can you get to the marina there?"

"Sure. But I've done a lot of work there. I might run into someone I know, even at this hour."

He seemed about to ask something, then shook his head. "Okay, somewhere else, then."

"The mission?" She grinned, the coolness vanished now. "I won't find *anybody* I know there!"

He couldn't help grinning back. "What a place to leave their car. Okay, that's it." He glanced at his watch. "Give me two hours." He looked suddenly serious. "You will be there?"

"I'm in this now. Why wouldn't I be?"

"I'm not sure I'd blame you if you weren't."

"I'd rather at least have a clue about what's going on," she said dryly. "You're stuck with me for now, Mr. McQuade."

"Maybe my luck's changing." It slipped out before he thought. "Two hours," he repeated abruptly.

She looked at him for a moment. "And if you don't show up in two hours?"

He looked away from a pair of tiger-green eyes that knew far too much about this ugly business. Too much for him to lie and deny the possibilities. "If something goes wrong ... don't wait. No later than five." He lifted his gaze to hers, his voice taking on that brisk, businesslike tone again. "Get out of here. Don't go back to the house, or to your father, or anywhere they'd expect, in case...they don't believe you don't know anything."

You mean if you can't convince them before they kill you, she thought grimly, wishing, not for the first time, that she'd had an ordinary childhood, without the knowledge that there was an ugly side of the world that made people no more than tools in a twisted, crazy game.

"Stay low until Linc gets home and you can get to him." His gaze turned suddenly intense. "But only to him. Don't talk to anyone else. Even on the phone. Got it?"

She raised an eyebrow, her mind racing, but after a moment she only nodded. His eyes went soft and warm. "You're quite a lady, Green-eyes." And then he was gone.

Shiloh drummed her fingers on the steering wheel, a nervous action that belied the even expression on her face. She fought the urge to look at the clock on the dash for the fifth time in as many minutes; she knew it was after five.

He'd had trouble. There was no other explanation. Damn, she should have asked him which motel. Oceanside wasn't that big, but it would still take time to check them all. Too much time, if he was in trouble. A vision of Moose standing over Con's lifeless body flashed through her mind. She shuddered.

No, damn it! She would not fall apart, would not sit here shaking helplessly, not as long as she could still move. She reached into the canvas carryall she'd moved up to the front seat and pulled out the .45. She checked the safety, then set it carefully on the seat, hidden by the bag. She reached for the ignition.

"You were supposed to be gone ten minutes ago."

She jumped, but managed to stop the startled cry that rose to her lips. Relief flooded her as he pulled open the passenger door and slid in, but she spoke coolly.

"Do you mind reserving the silent Indian act for the Mooses of the world, please? What happened?"

She saw amusement flicker in his eyes, but his voice was stern. "Moose didn't like the accommodations. Why are you still here?"

"I was just leaving." To her disgust, she sounded defensive.

"For where?"

When she didn't answer, he reached beneath the canvas tote and pulled out the .45.

"Never mind, I can guess. I told you to get the hell out of here, Shiloh."

"Do you always do what you're told?"

His mouth twisted into a wry smile. "About as often as you do, apparently." He thumbed the safety on, then looked over at her. "Just what were you going to do, Green-eyes?" he asked softly. Her lowered eyes and the slight pink tinge in her cheeks told him what she wasn't saying. "Just like that?" He repeated the words in a wondering tone.

Her chin came up. "What was I supposed to do? Go on my merry way and not look back? You could have been hurt, or dead...."

"Would it have mattered so much?"

His voice was husky and sent a little shiver through her. Get a grip, she snapped inwardly.

"Only if I wanted to sleep nights," she said, only raising her eyes to his when she was sure he would read nothing in them. "I owe you, too. For Linc."

A shutter dropped over his blue eyes, cutting off that odd intensity. "You owe me nothing," he said shortly. "Let's go."

"Where?"

"Start north."

Without another word she started the Blazer and wheeled it out of the parking area. They were on Interstate 5, all the way past the San Onofre Nuclear Generating Station, before he broke the silence with a muttered "Damn."

She glanced over at him. He was staring out the windshield, brows furrowed. That rugged jaw was set, his mouth tight, but she found herself looking instead at how the thick, dark mane of hair brushed the back of his neck and softened the chiseled lines of his face.

"Con?"

He looked up. He took a quick breath and shook his head.

"We'll have to dump your car soon. Sooner or later they'll figure out and start tracing what kind of car you have. They're too damned good not to have access to DMV."

She paled a little, but only nodded. That silent assent clawed at him.

"This stinks," he said succinctly. "I can't do a damned thing but wait."

"Wait?"

He let out his breath in a disgusted sigh. "The whole thing could unravel...." He swore softly again. "It's right in front of me, it has to be, so why the hell can't I see it?"

"Maybe you're too close to it right now."

He shrugged. "If Sam was here, he could start from the other end."

"Sam?"

"My boss." He looked a little startled, as if he hadn't meant to let the name slip out. "I'll just have to stall until he gets back."

"Stall?"

"Yeah. Do nothing." He spat the words out.

"Except stay out of their hands."

"Yeah." He chuckled grimly.

"So where are we going?"

"I don't know." He sounded bleak. "Until I figure out what—or who—went wrong."

He didn't have to explain. Shiloh knew he meant he couldn't trust anybody, couldn't use any of the resources he normally would.

"What about the loft?"

"The what?"

"The sail loft. Where I work. It's empty on Sunday, and there's a stove, a bathroom, even a place to pull the Blazer in out of sight."

He looked doubtful. "They found out where you lived, they would find that place, too."

"Maybe. But the office is in a different place, down at the marina. That's the address that's listed on everything. Not many people know where the loft itself is. It might give us at least a little time. There's not even a name on it. Jimmy likes to work in privacy."

"Jimmy?"

"*My* boss." She glanced at the freeway signs. "Now or never," she said, indicating the next off ramp. "That's the exit for the harbor."

Abruptly, he nodded. She changed lanes smoothly, heading for the lane marked Beach Cities. In the distance the Pacific glistened in the morning sun, and he saw the massive black bulk of the breakwater. Then he saw the sign with the arrow indicating Dana Point Harbor and Doheny State Beach, and soon they were down on the old Pacific Coast Highway. She drove with the sureness of someone long familiar with the area, making the turn off the highway onto a narrow, unmarked alleyway without hesitation.

"The marina office rent is ridiculous," she explained as they neared a long, low building, "and there isn't nearly enough room anyway, so Jimmy uses this place instead. It used to be a warehouse for a marine hardware store that went out of business."

"Go past it."

"What?"

"Drive past it. Then turn around and come back."

With a shrug she complied, going to the top of the small hill behind the building before she adeptly executed a turn in the narrow roadway.

"Kill the engine and coast in." He was checking the gun he'd taken from Moose, tucking it into his waistband. She did as he said.

"Park up here." He nodded to a spot just above the building. She didn't argue; he obviously wasn't taking anything for granted, and she couldn't fault him for that, no matter how unlikely she thought it was that anyone would find this place or connect it to him.

When she came to a halt by the side of the building, he opened his door. "If you hear anything that sounds wrong, start it up. If I'm not back here two minutes after that, get out of here." His face was harshly shadowed in the early morning light. "I mean it, Shiloh. I don't want you on my conscience."

"Just get back here and it won't be a problem."

She heard a low sound that could have been a chuckle; then he was gone. She rolled down her window, barely daring to breathe for fear she would miss some sound. Nothing broke the early morning silence except the occasional whir of tires on the Coast Highway three blocks away.

Twice her hand went to the door handle, and twice she made herself pull it away. She'd heard nothing; surely there would have been some sound? All she could hear was the hammering of her heartbeat and the distant passing cars. The irregular pace of the Sunday morning traffic seemed irritating, awkward, an out of step counterpoint to the steady trip-hammer in her chest.

Control, she repeated to herself, trying to slow the escalating pace of her pulse by using the order that had been her watchword since she'd been old enough to realize what the lack of control could do. She waited.

She caught movement from the corner of her eye and froze. The roof. God, there was someone on the roof.

Her hand hung in midair, stopped in the act of reaching for the .45. The glimpse she had gotten had played back in her mind like a recording, and she saw now the lithe movements, the lethal, coiled grace. Her sense of surprise that she had so easily recognized him was lost in relief as he reappeared at the edge of the building, levered himself over the side and dropped to the ground as easily as if it had been mere inches. He was back at the Blazer in seconds.

"All clear." She nodded and started the engine. "The loading dock door is on an opener?"

"In the glove box," she said, and he dug it out while she drove the Blazer into the narrow driveway and backed it up to the big, metal roll-up door. Moments later they were inside, the big door sliding down smoothly as Con hit the button on the remote control. The solid thump it made as it hit bottom gave her a comforting feeling of security.

Con slid out of the Blazer and looked around with interest. He'd never seen anything quite like this room, open and uncluttered by walls, full only of vast tables, open floor space, equipment that resembled some kind of medieval torture device, and roll upon roll of what he presumed was canvas. Or whatever they used for sails these days, he amended. Canvas was probably as outdated as the biplane.

Shiloh grabbed one of the bags of food and headed for the small kitchen alcove; Con followed. It was compact, carefully arranged, and looked highly efficient.

"Jimmy likes things shipshape," she said when she saw him inspect the facilities. "Sometimes he gets a rush job and ends up working twenty-four-hour days for a week. He eats and sleeps here."

She nodded at the worn but comfortable-looking couch next to the small table that sat against the wall under a poster for a past America's Cup race.

"Sounds rough."

"It is." She grinned suddenly. "But then he takes off for two weeks of sailing. How about some breakfast? I'm starved."

She refused his offer to help, and Con began to wander around the spacious building. For his purpose it was ideal; no windows, and the only way in except the heavy, metal door and one tightly bolted back door was the roof, which had several skylights.

He supposed it was ideal for its real purpose, as well, although he knew next to nothing about sailing or sails. Even so, he could see the efficiency of this operation. And the place was spotless. Shipshape, he thought, and wondered about this Jimmy who was Shiloh's boss.

He worked his way around to a corner near the kitchen—
or galley, he supposed—which seemed somehow different.
Here the fabrics were in riotous colors, roll after roll of
brilliant reds, blues, yellows and greens. There was a drafting table in addition to one of the huge platforms he'd
gathered were cutting tables, and on it was a large book
bound in bright red.

He flipped it open, finding the cover of a national sailing
magazine encased in protective plastic. It was a beautiful
color photograph of a sailboat, its bow sending water up in
a spray of white. But what drew the eye was not the boat itself, or even the sensation of speed engendered by that flying water; it was the huge, flying sail that billowed out in
front of it.

It was a sunburst of vivid color, each spoke pulling the eye
unrelentingly inward to a stark white center made pristine by
the riot of color around it, where the unmistakable corporate logo of one of the largest airlines in the world was nestled. It was striking, effective, a powerful piece of adver-
tising. He turned the page.

This time not a cover but just a photo, equally vivid, and
again of a billowing sail. This one was a parrot, feathered
in red and blue with such detail that it seemed as if the fabric had the iridescent sheen of the real creature. He saw the
name of a popular southern California restaurant for which
the bird was a symbol below the picture.

The next was an eagle, majestic wings spread, powerful
talons outstretched, so beautifully rendered it seemed as if
the magnificent bird was actually in flight. The name below that shot was immediately recognizable to anyone who
ever read the financial section of a newspaper.

The next page was so different, it took him a moment to
make the jump. It was a dragon, a whimsical, wide-eyed
creature straight out of a child's vision. Brightly, cheerfully
yellow, looking with pure astonishment at the puffs of
smoke that issued from its somehow gentle mouth, it was a
joyous salute to innocence. The caption read simply, "A
dragon lover." He'd been smiling down at it for a long time
before he realized it.

The rest of the book was more of the same: dazzling crayon colors or more subtle shading; designs that were dramatically impressive, or teasingly fanciful. He knew with certainty who was responsible for this corner of the loft, and knew he'd been right in guessing how she channeled all the emotion she seemed to keep so tightly under control.

"Should be ready in a minute. Toast and eggs okay?"

He looked up sharply; he'd been so engrossed that he hadn't heard her. He didn't like it. It made him nervous, as if he'd lost some of his edge.

"Uh . . . fine," he said, realizing she was waiting for an answer to her question. "You brought eggs?"

"I figured they'd just go bad if I left them. There were only four left, anyway."

"Oh." He glanced down at the photo album. "This is yours, isn't it." It wasn't a question, so she didn't answer. "When you said sail, I thought . . ." He shrugged, not sure what he'd thought.

"Jimmy does those. He's pretty well known for his racing sails. Locally, anyway. And the word's spreading."

He flipped back to the first page, to the magazine cover. "I can see that."

She grinned. "Jimmy hates it. Well, maybe not hates it, but he's a traditionalist. Sails serve a purpose, and that's making the boat achieve as many knots as the hull can take. He'll go along if somebody wants the upper panels dark, the theory being that the color absorbs heat and warms the air under it, helping to lift it in light air, but anything else is superfluous."

"But these are—"

"Frivolous. Cotton candy. Egotistical." She shrugged good-naturedly as she quoted her boss's words.

"They're beautiful!" His protest rang with a fervency that took her aback.

"Thank you," she said after a moment.

"If he hates them, why do you keep working for him?"

He sounds almost angry, Shiloh thought in amazement. "He gave me my start. And as much as he hates to admit it, they sell. And they're not cheap."

"They shouldn't be. But still—"

"I didn't say he didn't appreciate them. He just takes sailing a little more seriously than life. Besides," she added with a sudden grin, "he knows they're paying the bills and letting him play around with a lot of new stuff like Mylar polyester film and a few other things I can't even pronounce."

"Then he ought to have a little more respect," Con grumbled, not quite ready to be mollified.

Shiloh couldn't help laughing. "Oh, he's learning." She gestured to a framed photograph on the closest wall. "He even went to the unveiling of the dragon. It was for a friend of his father, who has a little girl who loves dragons."

Con smiled, remembering the caption below the dragon. There, in front of the sail, which fell in limp folds on the dock, stood an older man whom he assumed was the father she'd mentioned, with a clearly excited child of about five or six on his shoulders. Next to him, looking windblown and nearly as excited herself, was Shiloh.

His eyes lingered on her for a moment, his heart twisting inside him at the pure exuberance on that lovely face, his body surging to life at the sight of long, lovely, golden legs bared by a pair of silky nylon shorts. But then his smile faded as he looked at the man on her other side, the Jimmy he'd already decided he didn't like much. He liked him even less now.

The guy was perfect. The image of the California boy, blond, tanned, carefree, good looking, with that damned cocky grin that seemed indigenous to this part of the country. And he was standing too damned close to her, practically falling all over her.

"Actually," she was saying, "he only went because Jennifer—that's the little girl—begged him to. I think she had a crush on him."

"Great," he muttered, unsettled by the seemingly causeless anger that had boiled up in him. "I'm sure he's used to girls having crushes on him."

Shiloh laughed, and somehow it irritated him even more. "Just the little ones," she said lightly. "Mandy keeps him on a pretty short leash."

"Mandy?"

"His wife."

"His . . . He's married?"

"To my best friend. I introduced them. Oops." She lifted her head and sniffed. "I'd better get the eggs."

Con followed a little numbly, as unsure why his anger had so abruptly drained away as he had been about why it had risen in the first place. It must be lack of sleep, he told himself. And maybe the last of the fever, or flu, or whatever it had been that had knocked him for a loop.

He sat across from her at the small table, eating the eggs she'd scooped onto paper plates—"Jimmy hates dishes," she explained—and asked her more about her work.

"I'm strictly a landlubber," he said. "What do you call these?"

"They're spinnakers," she said, explaining between bites. "Supposedly the name came from an old racing boat in the 1800s. It was called the *Sphinx,* and they broke out this huge sail for running—that's sailing with the wind at your back," she put in at his look. "Anyway, they called it 'Sphinx's Acre' because it was so big, and somehow it ended up as spinnaker."

He kept asking questions, enjoying just listening to her. She obviously loved what she did; it showed in her voice, in her eyes, but most of all in the work itself. And she loved to sail.

"Inevitable, I suppose," she sighed. "Navy family and all that. Linc taught me to sail that summer after he came home from Vietnam." Her voice went soft, quiet. "He came a long way that summer. I didn't realize it then, what he was fighting. I only knew that the only time he didn't look . . . haunted, was when we were out on the water."

She smiled, a soft, reminiscent smile that began a hollow ache somewhere inside him. "I knew the Santa Barbara Channel inside out by the time I went back to school."

She glanced up then, as if she'd only now realized she'd been talking for so long. "I'm sorry. I don't usually run on like that."

"Don't apologize. I enjoyed it."

"You look tired, though. Why don't you get some sleep?"

"I've had more than you have. Why don't you rest?"

"I haven't been sick." She wrinkled her nose at him. "Nor did I get sat on by a Moose."

He laughed, but then glanced around the warehouse, and she knew what he was thinking.

"Even if they do find us, what are the chances they'll move before dark? Better get it now, just in case."

He knew she was right, but it was still with reluctance that he stretched out on the couch. He heard her tossing the used plates in the trash, then cleaning the skillet she'd used. He should have done that, he thought sleepily, but he was more tired than he thought.

"Con?"

"Hmm."

"Why didn't you tell me?"

His eyes opened. She was crouched beside the sofa, looking at him intently. He knew what she meant; she still wanted an answer to the question she'd asked that morning. He sighed inwardly. She deserved an answer, didn't she? An honest one?

"I didn't want you to think you owed me."

It came out more bitterly than he'd intended, but her expression didn't change.

"I...use people, Shiloh. Everyone, for whatever they can do to help me get the job done. Nothing else matters." His voice was tense, strained. "If they think they owe me, all the better. It just makes it easier. But it doesn't make it any prettier."

He picked at a thread on his sweater, a nervous motion that seemed incongruous coming from him. "You deserve better than that." He stared at that thread as if it were gold. "I didn't want it that way, not with you."

"Because of Linc?"

His head came up. He seemed about to say something else, then shrugged. "Yeah. Because of Linc."

Shiloh felt that odd sensation again, that letdown, as if she'd been hoping he would say something else. Like what? she asked herself scathingly as he turned his head away and closed his eyes. That he didn't want to use you personally? That it mattered not because of Linc, but because of you? Right, Reese. You left dreamland behind a long time ago. She got up and walked to her drawing board, where she sat staring at nothing for a long time.

Chapter 5

Con opened his eyes as he felt the presence beside him. She was there, in that green robe that made her eyes shimmer with matching color. Somewhere in the back of his mind he thought it odd that she'd brought it, but she was so beautiful as she stood there that he couldn't ask her why. He wondered why everything was so foggy, so blurred. Everything except her. She was crystal clear and glowing, and she made his blood begin to pulse in hot, heavy beats.

He levered himself up onto his elbows, wondering what had happened to the couch he'd fallen asleep on. And when the hell had he undressed? He looked up at her, the question on his lips, but she raised a finger to her own soft, sweet mouth and hushed him.

With slender, graceful hands that never hesitated, she reached for the zipper of the robe and drew it down with agonizing slowness. His eyes were riveted on the movement, on every inch of silken skin that was revealed as the fabric parted.

It stopped over the smooth, flat plane of her stomach, and her hands left the tab of the zipper. He could see the soft, full, inner curves of her breasts in the gap of the open-

ing, and her nipples were thrusting tautly against the green
silk. A small groan escaped him. God, what was she doing?
His body tightened, throbbed, began to ache in time with
the pounding of his blood in his ears.

Her hands went to the top of the robe, and without a
word she slipped it off her slender shoulders. It fell to the
floor in a lustrous puddle, and his breath stopped in his
throat as she stood before him. He moaned, reaching for
her, his body hard and demanding.

She was gone the instant he touched her. He felt a brief,
burning sensation, as if he had touched steam, and he sat up
with a jerk. Reality came crashing in, the mist of his dream
vanishing in a rush.

"Are you all right?"

Her voice came from one side, and he looked over to see
her sitting at her drafting table, sketches spread out in front
of her.

"Yes," he said tightly. "Fine."

Just stay there, he thought desperately. It might have been
a dream, but his body was still as aroused as if it had been
truth. Damn, what was wrong with him? If that vision had
lasted another minute he would have . . .

He shook his head sharply. He'd left that kind of thing
behind when he was fifteen. He stole another glance at her
as she gathered up what she'd been working on. She looked
so innocent, so unaware of her own appeal.

She is, he told himself savagely. It's you who's got the
problem. Just because your libido picked now to come out
of hiding, don't try to blame it on her.

He almost convinced himself it was only that, a case of
too long in cold storage, too long in that wintry, arid soli-
tude. Almost.

From that moment on he was as edgy as a caged tiger,
pacing, prowling. While she napped on the couch, he stayed
carefully away, not trusting himself to watch her sleep, not
with the image of that dream too fresh and real in his head.

He made himself go through it all again, from the day
Sam had told him what was happening at WestAir and sent
him in to find out how. Step by step he walked through it in

his mind, sometimes pausing to close his eyes as he rebuilt a scene in his head, trying to remember every word, every thing that was left unsaid, every nuance that might provide a clue, any clue, to how some of WestAir's most innovative designs were winding up in the hands of the competition.

He couldn't shake the feeling that the answer was right in front of him and he was too dumb to see it. The black hats, Shiloh had called them. He knew who the big one at WestAir was, but he wasn't the end of the chain. He could feel it, knew it as surely as he knew they would eventually find him again. And he knew how. He just didn't know who. Who was helping them.

She awoke in the early evening, sitting up sleepily to see him standing rigidly, with his head cocked to one side, listening.

"Dirt bikes," she said.

He spun around to look at her. "What?"

"In that empty lot. Two kids who live up the street a couple of blocks. They bring their dirt bikes down here and race them up and down the side of the little hill behind us. They're here almost every day. They've worn a path all the way down to the highway."

He relaxed then, at least as much as he could with her looking at him with eyes still wide from sleep, her hair slightly ruffled around her face.

"Are you hungry?" he asked, turning away.

"A little. I suppose it's out of the question to send out for pizza?"

He looked at her over his shoulder, then turned away again, but not before she saw the tension in his face.

"I was only kidding," she said softly. "I don't even like pizza." He didn't answer or look at her. "Look, if you don't get over feeling guilty for me being involved in this, it's going to be a very long...whatever it turns out to be."

She heard him let out a disgusted breath.

"There's not a thing you can do about it now, anyway. If you're going to worry, worry about something you can do something about."

He turned to look at her then. "Don't spin my wheels?"

She smiled as she recognized her brother's oft-used words. "Exactly. Stop feeling guilty, will you? Can you?"

He could stop feeling guilty about getting her into this; he hadn't really been himself when he'd somehow found his way to her door. What he couldn't stop was feeling guilty about the thoughts that kept sneaking into his mind the minute his guard was down, about that damned dream that had haunted him every minute since he'd awakened from it. Still... "I'll try," he offered.

"Good. What's for dinner?"

It turned out to be a big can of stew poured over the instant rice she'd thrown in at the last minute; it was surprisingly tasty and more than filling. They fixed it together, in companionable silence, and when they'd finished he got up without a word and cleaned up.

It was late when, after a long time spent pacing restlessly around the loft, he dropped down on the couch beside her. He saw that she had flipped on a light and was scanning the latest issue of the same magazine that had carried her sail on the cover.

"If the navy let women go on full sea duty, I get the feeling you'd be there."

She set down the magazine with a laugh. "I had delusions about that once. I used to think about being the first woman in a combat zone." She shrugged. "Then I had to grow up and realize it wasn't going to happen, at least not in time for me. But it was just as well. By then I realized that I didn't really like anything but sailboats."

The look in his eyes unsettled her a little. "Everybody has to make adjustments here and there, don't they?" she asked. "Or is this where you started out to be?"

He laughed, a little harshly, a little ruefully, rolling his eyes upward. "Not me. I was going to be an attorney. A prosecuting attorney. Clean the slime off the streets. Until I began to realize it didn't work that way."

"It didn't?"

His words were choppy, coming in unpracticed spurts. "Case after case. I saw people walk who were so dirty they smelled up the courtroom. I saw cops who blew their brains out because they just couldn't take it anymore.''

He ran a hand through his thick, dark hair. ''Everybody in my class was aiming for defense attorney. Or civil. Where the money is. To hell with justice. Just collect your fee, no matter what's right. Or who's guilty. It made me sick, but I kept on because I'd worked so damned hard for the scholarship. But I knew before I even graduated I couldn't handle criminal law.''

He stared at her suddenly, as if she were someone he'd never seen before. He looked shaken.

''Con?''

''I never . . .'' He stood up, turning his back on her. ''You and your brother,'' he muttered. ''I never told anybody all that, except him. And now I blab it to you.''

She wanted to ask him why, wanted to know why he was so cut off from the world. Whoever he worked for, he must have time off when he could forget it, leave it for a while.

''Con—'' She broke off when he threw up a hand. She could almost feel his sudden tension, the rigidity of every muscle as he cocked his head toward the roof. She held her breath.

He swore softly, viciously. He turned on her suddenly. ''Get in the truck. Stay there.'' He pulled out the gun he had stuck in his waistband at the small of his back. ''Now,'' he snapped, pulling her toward the Blazer when she didn't move. ''Don't start it until you're sure they know we know they're here. Have the opener ready.'' He grabbed her shoulders and turned her to face him. ''When I yell, or if you hear a shot, you hit it. I want you to be burning rubber getting out of here. Don't stop for *anything*. I don't care if you have to run over them, don't stop. Got that?''

''Con, why—''

''I mean it, damn it! You just get yourself out of here and don't stop for anything.''

''But—''

''Just keep going north. I'll find you. Don't make me worry about you, too!''

"I won't," she finally got in. "I just wanted you to take this." She held out the .45. "You might need the extra rounds."

He stared at her for a second, something warm and almost wistful in his eyes. What a ridiculous time to realize just how blue they are, Shiloh thought. Then he took the gun and the extra clip she held out to him.

"You've got the other one?"

She nodded, moving the revolver he'd taken from Moose's partner from the seat to her lap. She could hear them now, moving along the roof, toward the vulnerable skylights. She knew he was right, that the last thing he needed was to be thinking about her when he had who knew how many killers to deal with, but . . .

"Get in."

She climbed into the driver's seat. It took every bit of control she'd worked so hard for all her life to be able to speak at all. "You damn well better not get yourself killed, McQuade. I want that gun back."

He grinned suddenly, dimples flashing. "You'll get it, Green-eyes."

Then he was gone. She could tell which way he went by the fact that he hit the switch and plunged the loft into darkness. She heard a familiar creak and knew that he was climbing the ladder up to the rafters where the finished sails were stored until they were delivered. She realized he was going to try to ambush the intruders from there.

And maybe, just maybe, she could add to their confusion if she timed her exit exactly right. She heard the distant sound of breaking glass far above her and knew it had begun. She lifted the small revolver in her right hand, her left clutching the door opener and the steering wheel. She waited.

Her eyes had adjusted now to the eerie glow of moonlight through the glass in the roof. Not this skylight, then, she thought, and looked at the next. And there they were, three—no, four—dark, menacing shadows.

More glass broke, and the shadows moved. A rope uncoiled through the opening, and one, two, three of the shadows started down, sliding, aware they were at their most vulnerable point. Nothing happened. They were ten feet down from the ceiling, and Shiloh felt panic begin to rise. She fought it down.

And then things began to happen so fast that she had no time to think. She heard two shots in rapid succession. The .45 caliber shells echoed like cannon fire in the enclosed building. Incredibly, the three shadows and their severed rope plummeted the last ten feet to the floor. A very unprofessional scream issued from one of them as he slammed into one of the cutting tables. A third shot, and the fourth shadow at the skylight went reeling back.

One of the shadows on the floor got up, and Shiloh saw the muzzle of his gun flash as he fired. Upward. They knew where Con was now. Without a second thought she hit the door opener, then squeezed the trigger on the .38 she held. She fired once, twice, three times. She heard the distinctive twang of a ricochet and a hoarsely shouted curse.

She shifted the gun to free her right hand and started the Blazer, sparing a split second to glance at the door; it was almost high enough.

She saw one of the shadows running toward her. Before she could switch the gun back, the .45 boomed again. The man fell forward as if hit by some giant, unseen fist.

Shiloh threw the Blazer forward, burning rubber as Con had asked. Her last glance back showed her a lean figure pulling himself up to the broken skylight. She realized what he was going to do and scrambled for the door opener she had carelessly tossed. She found it, hit it, just as she cleared the door.

More shots. More glass breaking, somewhere close. Something stung her cheek, her neck. She could smell the tires, could hear them squeal as she made the turn out of the loft. A thud and a scream. She kept going, Con's words echoing in her ears.

Headlights flashed on as a car on the street pulled up, blocking the driveway. She yanked the wheel around and jammed the accelerator to the floor, praying she had enough room. She ran up over the curb, felt the Blazer shudder as metal clipped metal. Then she was clear, on the sidewalk and heading up the hill. She heard the roar of the other car and saw the headlights swing in an arc as the driver tried to turn to come after her.

Then he had done it, and the lights were closing in fast. With a whispered prayer to no one in particular, she threw the wheel to the left. The Blazer's wheels thumped, bit. Then she was over the slight embankment. She barely heard the crash behind her; she was fighting the wheel every foot of the way as the truck careened down the path worn by the dirt-bikers.

With a thump that severely tested the suspension, she went over the curb and down onto the roadway. She sat there in the bike lane, peering back over her shoulder, not daring to believe that that malevolent pair of headlights had not followed her down. A shadow broke from the building to her left, and her foot twitched on the accelerator. Then something about the way it moved warned her, and she backed off.

"Slide over, Green-eyes," he said, pulling open the door.

She did, and he slid in beside her. He eased the Blazer out onto Coast Highway and proceeded at a decorous pace. Shiloh sat in silence, trying to stop the shaking that threatened to overcome her. She wouldn't, she insisted silently, clamping her trembling hands between her knees. She would *not* get hysterical.

Con's eyes flicked constantly from the road to the rearview mirror. A sheriff's unit passed, going swiftly the other way, but the deputy didn't seem to look twice at them. Con waited until it was out of sight, then ducked onto the first side street, then onto another, then another. He eased the Blazer to the curb. Shiloh squeezed her hands tighter.

"Shiloh."

His voice was soft, her name a caress on his lips. She looked up. "You've got to help me again. Where are we?"

She looked out the window. She was almost afraid to try to talk, afraid her terror would make it impossible. She swallowed and tried.

"Almost to the harbor."

She blinked in surprise; she hadn't sounded nearly as bad as she'd expected. She shifted her gaze to him. He looked strained in the faint glow from a distant streetlight.

"Damn it!" He hit the wheel fiercely. "It's a stacked deck. Every hand, they already know what's been dealt. Whoever the connection is, he's got access to everything. There isn't a place in the damned state to hide."

"What about out of it?"

He turned to look at her. He'd known she was on the edge, had resisted the urge to comfort her, afraid it would send her toppling over. But she was steady now, the shaking he'd noticed gone, her eyes meeting his evenly. God, she was incredible.

"What do you mean?"

"A boat."

He looked at her, his mind racing. "What boat?"

"It belongs to a friend of mine. He's in Europe. He gave me the use of it in exchange for keeping it up for him." She leaned forward and dug through the canvas tote that had wound up on the floor in her crazy slide down the hill. In a moment she came up with a set of keys. "I didn't know what to do with these, but I didn't feel right just leaving them."

He moved toward her, arms out as if to hug her, but stopped himself. "Green-eyes, you have all the instincts of a natural. Where is this boat?"

Warmed by his words, she pointed toward the harbor. "At the yacht club. Wayne's a high roller."

She gave him directions, and in less than ten minutes they were pulling into a parking lot. Con could see row upon row of boat slips stretching into the distance, laid out in different directions on each side of a small bridge. There were lights on, and the sound of music coming from the building on the edge of the water, but the parking lot seemed empty of people.

"This is it?"

She nodded, gesturing toward the docks. "She's right down there, on *G* dock."

After a moment, he nodded. Then he wheeled the Blazer back out of the lot. Shiloh looked at him.

"I'm going back to that restaurant we passed," he said, for once answering her question before she could voice it. "We'll leave the truck there. It's busier there and it won't stand out so much."

She nodded and said no more as they drove to the water-front restaurant. He pulled the Blazer into a dark, isolated spot and sat for a moment, looking around. The parking area was concealed from the road by a high, thick hedge, but he waited, anyway. When nothing happened, he shut off the motor and opened the door.

Shiloh glanced at him curiously when he walked over to the front of a car parked a few spaces away, knelt, and fiddled with something for a moment. Then, carrying something she couldn't see, he came back and knelt at the back of the Blazer, then went to the front. She didn't realize what he'd been doing until he stood up with the Blazer's license plates in his hands. She slid out of the front seat and walked back to confirm her guess; he had switched her plates with one from a nearby car.

"It might slow them down a little," he said when he saw her look. "I only took the front plate from the other one, so hopefully they won't notice it right away."

After a moment, Shiloh nodded.

"I'll see what I can salvage of the food that's still here," she said, climbing into the back. When she came out again she found him standing by the driver's door, staring at the lower corner of the windshield. She had known it was broken, from some rock thrown up on her trip down the hill.

Her thoughts stopped abruptly when she caught a glimpse of his face. He looked utterly bleak.

"Con?" She followed his gaze, only then seeing the small, round hole in the center of the starburst of cracks.

A bullet hole. So that was what she'd heard. She stifled a shiver, but that look on his face made her go on as if she'd known all along.

"Come on," she urged. When he didn't move, she thrust the bag of groceries she held into his arms. He took them reflexively, and it seemed to be enough to get him moving. She went back for the other bag, then returned for her suitcase. He took it from her without a word, and she reached into the truck and pulled out the canvas bag.

He followed her silently down to the dock, holding the other bag while she unlocked the gate at the top of the gangway. She led the way to one of the slips near the end and put the bags on top of a set of steps built onto the dock.

In the dark he couldn't tell much more than that the boat was about thirty-five or forty feet long, so when he followed her down the steep stairway into the main cabin and she flipped on a light, he looked around in surprise.

Minus what he'd learned from her, what he knew about sailboats could fit on a matchbook. But even he could see that this was something special. He could stand up to his full height of six-one and still clear the ceiling by enough to be comfortable. Wood gleamed, warm brass shone softly, and there were cushions of rich green velour that looked luxuriously inviting. The cool sheen of marble glowed unexpectedly from the countertops.

"Whew," he whistled softly as he watched Shiloh poking around in the cupboards in the galley.

"Isn't she beautiful?" Her voice echoed oddly from the cubbyhole she was reaching into. She looked back over her right shoulder at him. "She's a Hans Christian. Class all the way, and she sails like a dream. You could take her around the world, if you wanted."

"I'd rather not, thank you." It was a beautiful boat, and larger than he'd expected, but around the world in anything less than the *Queen Elizabeth II* was too much for him.

She laughed, the light, cheerful sound of someone back on home ground after a sojourn into nightmare. Suddenly weary, he succumbed to the invitation of the thick, soft cushions and sagged down on the bench seat across from the main table.

"I'll check the supplies, but Wayne always believes in keeping her stocked in case he wants to take off at a moment's notice."

"And who is this Wayne who's so obliging?"

"Wayne DeWitt. He owns an electronics company, hence all the gear." She gestured over her shoulder.

Con looked in the direction she indicated, toward a small cubby with a built-in chair, which contained what had to be every electronic device known to man. He recognized the basics, sonar, radar, barometer and radio. Two radios, in fact. He filed that away in his head. The rest was a conglomeration he didn't even speculate on.

"He's starting to export to Europe, so he's there to set things up. His company is really taking off. I'm glad for him. He's worked very hard."

Con glanced around at the rich, expensive-looking vessel. "And plays hard, too, I gather."

"He's earned it," she said from the galley, a little sharply. "The company almost went under, and he pulled it back up with sheer determination and backbreaking work. He bought the *Phoenix* when he'd doubled his original worth."

He shifted uncomfortably on the seat, taken aback by her spirited defense of the man. Admiration for her loyalty warred with a rather unkind curiosity about what DeWitt had done to deserve it. Irritation he didn't understand rose in him again, but he only muttered, "Sorry."

"It's okay. It must look like that if you don't know."

She left the galley and came to sit on the curved settee that wrapped around the teak table across from him. He was studying his battered tennis shoes as if he'd never seen them before, engrossed in a futile battle to halt an anger he couldn't figure out.

"We're in good shape," she said. "Plenty of everything that isn't perishable. There's even beer in the fridge."

"Great. Then we—" He stopped, staring. He'd only then looked up at her, only then seen her in the light. "God, Shiloh, why didn't you tell me you were hurt?" He reached for her hands and pulled her over beside him.

"I am?" She looked blank.

Con's stomach had begun churning at the first sight of the blood on the left side of her face. It had trickled over the delicate skin to her neck, where another small stream joined it and flowed down her slender throat to dampen the neck of her sweatshirt. With hands that trembled slightly he tilted her head back, turning her cheek to the light.

"Looks like a glass cut." He swore under his breath. "Probably when that bullet came through the windshield."

Her brow furrowed as she tried to remember those frantic moments. "I do remember something stinging," she began, her hand automatically going to her cheek.

"Don't touch it. There may still be some glass in there. Are you hurt anywhere else?" His tone was sharper now, brisker, in command.

"No, I—"

"Is there a first-aid kit around?"

She nodded. "I'll get—"

"You'll sit. Where is it?"

She pointed. "Under the top step."

He turned and crossed to the stairway. Sure enough, the step was hinged, and when he lifted it the white box with the red cross was inside. Smart, he admitted grudgingly, for it to be where you could reach it from inside or out. He vaguely noticed that even the inside of the compartment was finished in that same, rich wood and had to agree with her. This boat was class all the way.

He made her sit at the navigation station, where there was a high intensity of light. He gently wiped away the blood. He probed at the cuts, removed one small sliver with exquisite care, holding the tweezers rock steady. It was a triumph of control; inside he was shaking. And furious with himself, despite his promise to her earlier.

"This is going to sting," he warned her as he poured disinfectant on a piece of gauze. She sucked in her breath when the liquid hit the cuts, but made no other sound.

"Anyone ever tell you that you're a master of understatement?" she asked dryly when he'd finished.

"I'm sorry." He didn't look at her as he replaced everything neatly in the kit. "About everything."

Shiloh sighed. "I thought we settled that. No wheel spinning."

"So it's harder than I thought." He slammed the box shut and went to put it back.

"It's only a cut. Not even worth a bandage. Quit it."

He let the lid of the step drop back into place, irritated that it was so well built it didn't even bounce. Boy, you're really on the edge if that's all it takes to set you off, he told himself. And with a determined effort he forced himself into a semblance of calm.

"Sorry. Just edgy, I guess." Why am I always apologizing to her? Because you're always being a jerk, that little voice answered. Shut up, he snapped inwardly. Where the hell were you when I needed you?

"Me, too. Let's forget it, okay?"

He looked at her, sitting there so calmly. You didn't need me at all, the little voice said smugly. Shut up, he repeated, without much emphasis. He walked back and sat down where she had been, across from the bench that ran along the wall. Or whatever they called it on a boat. He studied the floor this time, seeing the exquisite workmanship of the narrow teak strips.

After a moment she spoke. "Do we sit tight or cast off?"

He raised his head. "They're too damned good, Shiloh. It should have been hard for them to find me at your place, but they did it in days. It should have been harder for them to find the loft, and they did that in one. And now they have a chance of finding your car to help them along." He laughed harshly. "That means they should be here in about an hour."

"Con...my father...if they think we might go there..."

"I know. I've been thinking about that, too."

"Then you think they might find him?"

His mouth twisted into a bitter smile. "I'm through underestimating them. He could be a lever for them, the only one they've got."

"A lever? But why would they think he meant anything to you? Why wouldn't they go after someone who does?"

"Because there isn't anyone," he said briefly, in a cold, flat tone that forbade any emotion, any sympathy for what the bleak words revealed. "But they know you're in this now, even if they don't know why. So now they've got their lever, if they can find it."

She paled but didn't speak. As if it were a visible thing, he saw her draw on some inner strength and steady herself. Amazing, he thought. She's just like Linc. And her father. A cool customer. Blood, he thought with a twinge of bitterness. Blood will tell.

"You can't use a lever if you can't find the person you want to use it on," he said abruptly, grimly.

"So we run."

He let out a long breath. "For now. Just until my boss gets back." He ran a hand through his tousled hair. "It's his company, his people, he's got to make the decision." He felt her eyes on him. "They won't hurt your father, if they do go for him. They need him. Hell," he said tiredly, "maybe they won't even think of it."

"But you don't believe it."

"They haven't missed a damn thing yet."

"Can I at least . . . warn him?" He looked at her doubtfully. "The radio. Marine operator. They wouldn't be expecting that, would they? I'll wait until we're offshore."

He hesitated, then nodded. It was a risk, but he had no right to deny her. She had forgiven him for the danger he'd put her in; if anything happened to her father, he knew she would never forgive him again. He didn't stop to think why it would matter so much, since, after this was over, he would never see her again. He didn't want to think about that time, not now.

"Then let's go."

He looked up as she got to her feet, clearly anxious to get started. He studied the length of the boat. "Can you really sail this thing by yourself?"

"She's cutter-rigged with roller furling. Piece of cake." She eyed him pointedly. "Provided, of course, my deckhand does what he's told."

He laughed, startling himself; he hadn't figured there would be much to laugh about in their situation. He got up and threw her a salute. "Aye, aye, cap'n," he said with a grin. "But you'll have to tell your dumb deckhand in English. All that nautical talk is beyond my limited capabilities.''

She grinned back. ''I'd say you're trainable. Might even make it to first mate someday.''

''Oh, I'll work hard,'' he said with exaggerated earnestness.

''That,'' she said dryly, ''I can guarantee.'' She headed to the steps. ''Close the bow hatch, will you? I'll fire her up.''

He nodded, then waited until she'd put her foot on the first step. ''That's the pointy end, right?''

She looked back sharply. His effort at a straight face crumpled, and a grin tugged at his mouth. She tried to look angry and failed; as she went up on deck she was laughing.

Con stood staring after her. They were about to take off in a boat in the middle of the night, with her sailing it virtually alone. She'd been run out of her home, shot at, cut up, had driven straight down the side of a hill, she was worried to death about her father, and she could still laugh.

And make him laugh. He didn't recognize himself in this man who had taken to engaging in lighthearted verbal dueling with her quick wit. It was a kind of carefree silliness he'd never known, and it intrigued him even as it bemused him. It seemed absurd in the midst of the mess they were in. Then he heard the distinctive sound of a diesel power plant starting, and, like a good deckhand, he went to obey the captain's order.

Had she been blindfolded, Shiloh would still have known the second they cleared the breakwater. She felt the deck lift beneath her feet as the swell increased, felt the breeze as they left the protection of that wall of rock. As sweetly as ever, the *Phoenix* responded to the wheel, and they made the turn and were out of the harbor.

It was an almost surreal scene, the moonlight dancing over the quiet water, the empty sea spread before them. They had passed one cruiser coming in, loaded with slightly tipsy partygoers, but the ocean beyond the harbor belonged to them on this peaceful Sunday night. The farther they went, the more it changed, until the surreal became real, and the chaos they had gone through before became the unreality.

Gradually, as the distance between them and the receding land increased, Con began to relax. If their luck held until they were out of sight of the coast, if they could just get that much breathing room . . .

He listened but could barely hear the steady thrum of the engine. She had told him it ran quiet, that that was one of the beauties of the little ship; she hadn't exaggerated. He had been dividing his time between watching behind them and searching the empty expanse of black water before them. She said she preferred to motor at night, to take advantage of their greater maneuverability under power just in case they came upon something in the darkness.

"Something?" he had asked, a little warily.

"Debris, McQuade," she had answered with a grin, "not the Loch Ness monster."

He had grinned back, shrugging. "Told you I was a landlubber."

It was then that he had at last begun to relax. He just watched her, liking the way she looked standing at the big, traditional teak wheel, the breeze of their movement blowing her hair, the look of enjoyment visible on her face even in the moonlight. Especially in the moonlight.

After a while she bent to fiddle with a piece of equipment, then came back to sit beside him on the cockpit seat. He looked from her to the unattended wheel and back.

"Automatic pilot, I hope?"

She laughed and nodded. Damn, he was beginning to like that sound.

"Where are we going?"

"On this course? We'll hit Hawaii in about three weeks."

He stared at her, then at the compass, then back at her. He caught the gleam of even, white teeth as she failed to smother her grin. He chuckled ruefully. And halfheartedly. The thought of sailing to Hawaii with her didn't sound nearly as absurd as it should have.

"I thought we'd head for the windward side of Catalina. Not many people there during the week, and there're a dozen little coves to hide in and never see a soul."

A rather acid question about her having hidden in them with the worthy Wayne rose to his lips, but he bit it back and merely nodded. The *Phoenix* chugged steadily on. It was a while before he spoke again.

"Shiloh?"

"Hmm?"

"That was a hell of a stunt you pulled back there."

She shifted to look at him; he could see the silvery light reflected in her eyes. "You mean my little trip down the hill?"

He let out a little breath. "That, too. You wrapped those two guys around a pole trying to follow you."

"Good," she said simply.

"I meant laying down that cover fire. You could have gotten out without a scratch if you hadn't done that."

"I didn't hit anybody. I just wanted to distract them."

"You did. I was pinned down. That one guy came a little too close for comfort."

"So did the one heading for me, the one you dropped. And speaking of stunts, how about that cowboy act with the rope?"

She saw him lift a shoulder in a careless gesture. "I thought it might work, with the .45 and three of them on the rope. It did." He looked at her for a moment. "What made you close the door?"

"I saw you go out the skylight."

He shook his head. "So you locked them in. Green-eyes, you amaze me."

The admiration in his tone warmed her again. "You're kind of impressive in action yourself, Mr. McQuade. Tell me, how did you get into this line of work?"

The silence stretched, her words hanging in the air as he lifted one foot to brace it on the cockpit seat and rested his elbow on his upraised knee. She wasn't surprised; when it came to himself, he had the conversational tendencies of granite. Long after she had given up expecting an answer, he spoke. The words came slowly, awkwardly at first, the very sound of them telling her how unaccustomed he was to talking like this.

"When I left school, I decided to try corporate law. Nice, clean business deals, I thought. All on the up-and-up. Talk about naive." He gave a little snort of laughter. "I went to work in the legal department of a company in Denver. After six months I was bored to tears. After a year I was ready to quit. All I ever did was open mail and file it. That was the highlight of my day, filing."

"You?"

"Yep. Connor McQuade, boy clerk, filer and gofer."

She couldn't picture it. "I'm surprised you lasted a whole year."

"I was still pretty naive. I kept thinking it would change someday." His voice was full of self-mockery, although the words were coming more easily now. "Then I stumbled onto some evidence that somebody was skimming. I poked around a little and found out how, and where it was going. So I went to my boss with it." He paused, and she could see the wry twist of his lips. "There was only one problem."

"He was in on it?"

"He *was* it. He'd been doing it for years, had a nice pile in a Swiss account. I was too damned stupid to see it."

"Who would ever have suspected it?" she protested. He raised an eyebrow at the quickness of her defense. "What happened to him?"

"Nothing."

She looked puzzled. "Why? If you had the proof—"

"He made sure I didn't have a chance to use it. He meant to make it permanent, but his aim was off."

"He . . . shot you?"

"By the time I came around in the hospital, he was gone. Along with any trace of what he'd been doing. Probably living high on the Riviera somewhere."

And you haven't trusted anyone since, she thought with instinctive certainty. Except maybe my brother. "But you're still doing it. Going after the bad guys, I mean. Why?"

He chuckled ruefully. "You mean after my inauspicious start?"

"No," she said softly. "After he almost killed you."

He automatically started to dissemble, then shut his mouth. There wasn't any point in denying it when he knew she'd seen the jagged scar. Among other things.

The heat that spurted through him at that memory made his body clench, and once more he fought the image of that vivid, erotic dream. For one of the few times in his life, talk was welcome.

"I lived," he said shortly. "But the old man who owned the company sold out after the dust settled, and I was out of a job. I was in that hospital bed, trying to figure out how I was going to pay for it, when the guy he sold out to walked in. Mr. Wills had called him about me. He offered me a job right then."

He dragged a hand over his tousled hair. "Needless to say, I took it. I had to. But I was glad later. The new owner knew exactly what he wanted me to do, and he arranged for me to get some pretty heavy training." He smiled crookedly. "Some of it private, from . . . soldiers of fortune, I suppose, and then some high-level military training, which is practically unheard of for a civilian. My boss has a lot of clout." He shrugged. "I've been with him ever since."

"Sam?"

He nodded. "He's a straight arrow. Seven years, and he's never let me down once."

So there was at least someone else he trusted, she thought. But whoever Sam was, he hadn't been there this time. Whatever it was, whatever Con had been doing—and she had begun to doubt rather sourly that she would ever know, if she left it to him to tell her—Sam wasn't there to help.

"Never let you down until now," she said.

He shook his head. "He didn't know it was going to come apart. Neither did I. It shouldn't have. Not so soon. I'd only been on it two weeks."

"On what?"

He looked at her for a moment, then looked away, studying the horizon as if he expected it to change. "I can't,

Shiloh. You know that. As long as you don't know anything—''

"—I'm a sitting duck. And they won't believe I don't
know anything, anyway. *You* know that.''

She waited, and when he didn't answer, she got to her
feet. He still didn't trust her. "I'm going to call my father," she said, and went below, the taut straightness of her
back speaking eloquently of her feelings.

Chapter 6

He heard her raise the marine operator. He stared ahead, his emotions in turmoil, his common sense trying to battle them down. She'd done so much already, saved his butt more than once, she deserved his trust, didn't she? Keep her out of it, his common sense ordered. Trust nobody.

He heard the call go through and thought suddenly that he should have warned her not to say too much. But before he could call out to her, he heard a deep, rumbling voice coming over the small speaker of the VHF radio.

"Yo."

"Hi, Daddy." It was endearing, that childhood term, and he remembered how he'd felt that night when Linc had first told him about his family.

"Shy, is that you, girl?"

"It's me, Daddy. How are you?"

"On an even keel, baby. Is something wrong? I didn't expect to hear from you again so soon."

"Can't I call my own father without something being wrong?"

Con heard a low, indulgent chuckle. "You do, baby, but not usually twice in a week, and not usually via ship-toshore. When you're at sea, you're too wrapped up to think of your old dad.''

"You should know."

The chuckle became a hearty laugh. "Aye, that I do, baby, that I do. Where are you?"

"In the Pacific."

"Oh, feeling smart-alecky, are we?"

"No. Daddy?" Her voice had changed, and her father didn't miss it.

"Come clean now, girl. What is it?"

"Remember the 'black hat' game?"

The deep voice was suddenly taut. "Yes. Why?"

"I've been...wondering. The person I'm with knows the rules, but I was afraid you might have forgotten."

"Some things you never forget." He didn't know the man, but Con knew that tone, knew it too well.

"Good. Maybe you could ask my brother to write them down and send them to me, if you hear from him."

"A big if, but I will. Do you have all the pieces you need to play?"

"Not quite. Some of them are missing, but they may turn up anywhere, when you least expect it. You know how it goes."

"Yes." Worry crept into the deep voice. "Do you?"

"I had a great teacher. I have to go, Daddy. I love you."

"I love you, too, baby. Take care."

"I will. You, too."

Con stared down the hatchway at her as she hung up the radio microphone. And he had thought he should warn her not to say too much. She had done it, in words an outsider would never understand. Her father was warned, and she'd even managed to sneak in a call for Linc. He shook his head in wonder as she came back up to the wheel as carefully as if the automatic pilot had suddenly gone haywire.

"The 'black hat' game?" he finally asked.

Her voice was cool, impersonal. "It was the game he invented to teach us what to do if anybody ever came for us. First Linc, then me. He called them the 'black hats.' It was easier for a child to understand."

"And the rules?"

"The rules are that there aren't any rules. You do whatever you have to do. He thought we were better off knowing what we were up against than being caught by surprise. We were children, but he trusted us. We would have died rather than let him down."

Ouch, Con thought. Yet hadn't her father been proven right? Where would she be—hell, where would *he* be—if she hadn't reacted the way she had? It all would have ended back there in her living room.

"Your father is a very wise man." His words were quiet, soft.

She turned to look at him. "Yes, he is."

He sighed. "I just wanted to keep you out of it. But you're right. You're already in it."

"Up to my neck," she said, but not coldly anymore.

"And a lovely neck it is." Only when she looked sharply at him did he realize he'd said it out loud; he was grateful for the darkness masking his face.

Shiloh was thankful herself for the silver wash of moonlight as she felt her cheeks heat. "Just how far back is that Irish blarney?" she asked lightly.

She didn't even convince herself; she knew he didn't throw out idle flattery. The knowledge did nothing to ease her reaction.

"Not far enough, I guess," he muttered.

She sat back down, a careful two feet away from him. This is ridiculous, she lectured herself. She'd had her share of flattery from men over the years and had brushed most of it off uncaringly, wishing they would compliment her on something worthwhile rather than that chance arrangement of features and vivid coloring they seemed so fond of.

This man had done just that since the first glint of admiration had lit his blue eyes. He made her feel competent and in control. So why was it the hint that he might find her attractive made her blush, made her pulse begin to flutter? It made no sense at all.

"Shiloh?"

"What?"

"I'm sorry." Again. "I promised not to underestimate you. But I've never come across anybody quite like you." He managed a slight smile. "Just keep kicking me. I'll get it through my head."

"Linc said you were . . . independent."

"Why do I get the feeling that's the edited version?"

She grinned suddenly. "Well, he did say a few other things. I just didn't remember them until now."

"I'll bet. We didn't hit it off at first."

"So he said."

"He told you a lot, I gather."

"Everything but your name." She looked at him, hesitant; then her curiosity won out. "He also said he envied you."

"Me?" He was startled. "What the hell for?"

She wondered at his astonishment, but merely explained. "He said it would be heaven to be responsible only for getting the job done, and only to one man instead of an admiral, the entire navy and the federal government."

"Oh. That." He shrugged. "It has its good points. And its bad ones."

"Like now? No backup?"

Con paused, then nodded. "Normally, there would be. Sam's got some good men working for him."

He paused again, then made himself go on. He had to, he thought. She'd earned it. Besides, she was Linc's sister. Blood ran true; who knew that better than he did? He didn't admit how much of his decision was based on the need to keep that chill in her voice from being directed at him again.

"I was undercover at one of Sam's companies. He sent me in when two new projects wound up in production by the competition while they were still in the final testing stages at WestAir. Sam's not much of a believer in coincidence."

"I can see—" She stopped, her eyes widening. "WestAir? Sam? Your boss is Sam West?"

He hesitated, then let out a small breath and nodded. Shiloh sat back. "Whew." She gave him a sideways look. "Then he *is* as straight as everybody says?"

He nodded. "And everybody who works for him plays by his rules."

"And when they don't, that's where you come in?"

"Something like that."

"'The Troubleshooting Division,'" she quoted, remembering.

Con winced. The article in a national magazine that had quoted Sam's effusive praise of his privately recruited and trained "Problem Management Force" had been published over three years ago, but the nickname coined by the writer, bolstered by the article's highlighted list of impressive successes, seemed to have stuck for good.

"You were working for him in the Philippines?"

He nodded again. "That sonar tracker was built by SeaTech, another WestCorp company. When it got sabotaged, Sam took it very personally."

"So did the navy."

"So I found out," he said with a grin.

"And so did the black hats." The sudden solemnity of her voice told him that she was thinking of how nearly things had ended in disaster. Whatever instinct had made him move when he had seen that glint of light on metal at Linc's back, he was glad of it now, not only for the sake of the man who had, unexpectedly, become a friend, but for this lovely, spirited woman who loved that friend so much. That old longing, that ache he'd thought he'd conquered long ago, rose up suddenly, fiercely. He beat it back down.

"—not a military project this time?"

"No. The first one was. That's why the FBI went in. But this one was strictly commercial. And, like most things Sam touches, very profitable. Only the wrong people are making the profit."

"There's no way it could really be coincidence?"

"Similar projects, yes. Exact down to the smallest specifications, no."

"Somebody sold out." He nodded, chilly eyes awash in silver moonlight. "And you found out who?"

"Apparently." She looked at him quizzically. "I only had a suspicion, a gut-level feeling, I guess. I hadn't even started to dig. I didn't have any proof yet. I still don't."

"Except that they tried to kill you."

"Yes."

"And did kill an FBI agent."

"Yes." He took a breath. "I know that now. I always suspected it, even though there was no evidence. But the Feds were convinced it was an accident, because their guy had already turned in a clean report on WestAir, and there was no reason for them to kill him."

He shifted on the cockpit seat. "I don't know if the FBI man was really convinced they were clean, or if they bought him off. And then killed him as insurance that he wouldn't talk. We may never know."

She was silent for a long moment. The steady swish of the bow spray as the cutter sliced through the gentle swells was oddly comforting, a touch of reality on the ghostly moonlit ocean. She looked out at the silver path that beckoned them on, then back at the firm, chiseled planes of his face. One seemed as unreal, as impossible, as the other.

"Somebody blew your cover, didn't they?" Her voice was quiet with the finality of one who already knew the answer.

She was right, he thought, but, driven by a curiosity he didn't understand, he asked anyway. "What makes you think I didn't just screw up, do something to make them tumble to me?"

She shook her head slowly. "No."

"That's it? Just like that?"

She smiled at the recurrence of the words; a lot of things seemed to be happening that way. "Just like that."

Her instant bestowal of faith shook him. It was an act so near to impossible for him that he couldn't help but be awed at the ease with which she did it. When he went on, his voice was a little unsteady.

"You're right, though. I never had a chance to tip my hand." He let out a long breath. "It's the only explanation. Somebody tipped them off."

"Somebody who knew you?"

"I thought so at first. Somebody who'd worked some-where else I'd been, or at Sam's headquarters in Denver. I even thought it could have been innocent. A 'What's he doing here?' to the wrong person."

"Until?"

"Until Moose said they'd been given your address."

"By who?"

He shrugged. "I know who. What I don't know is where *he* got it."

"The guy who's running things?" she asked.

"It has to be. But…no matter who it is, there should have been no way for them to…" He stopped, letting out a long breath that sounded oddly strained.

"No way to what?"

"To find you."

"You did."

"That was different. I knew where you were."

"You…did?"

He was silent for a moment. "When I woke up in the hospital in Subic Bay, Linc was there. He was writing you a letter. I saw the address."

"And remembered it?" She sounded incredulous, and he shrugged.

"Occupational hazard." Then he grinned. "Actually, I was in no shape to remember the number, but I knew the street, and Linc had described the house. 'It's the one the flowers love,' he said."

Shiloh was a little taken aback by this touch of pastoral appreciation from her very tough, very worldly brother. She was taken aback that that same, very protective brother had opened up enough to discuss her at all; clearly the respect and liking Con felt for him were returned. Both thoughts left her feeling absurdly pleased.

Con's grin had faded, and the strain had returned to his voice. "They shouldn't have known you existed."

"But they found out. Which means?"

"I'm not sure, exactly." His tone made it clear that he didn't care for the possibilities. "They shouldn't even have been able to find out about Linc. Sam doesn't keep that kind

of thing in writing. Most of the PMF work is undocu-
mented. So there's not a damned thing on our end that
anybody could find to show that Linc and I had even
worked together, let alone anything about you.''

"Who knew that you had worked with him?"

"A handful of people, most of them in the navy." He
rubbed a hand over his beard-roughened jaw, wondering
idly if the wonderful Wayne kept a razor on this tub. "On
our side, only me, Sam and, after the fact, Joe Selkirk. He's
Sam's top aide. Ex-navy himself. He and Linc knew some
of the same people." He let out a short breath. "I don't get
it. There's no way those goons could have known about you.
Nobody knew I'd ever laid eyes on Linc after we got back.
I never contacted him at his office, and vice versa."

"Of course."

The habits of a lifetime were hard to break, as Shiloh had
learned early on. She was twelve years old and on a vacation with friends before she learned that not every father
checked the motel room for bugs other than the multi-
legged kind, not to mention an escape route.

Con shrugged, admitting it. "Levers," he said, summing
it up in a word. "There's no evidence of a connection that
would have led them to you. Hell, there isn't a connection
for them to find."

"Wasn't," she amended softly.

"Yeah." He let out a disgusted sigh. "I took care of that,
didn't I?"

"No wheel spinning," she repeated. "Who knew you
were going into WestAir?"

"Sam."

"Only Sam?"

He nodded. Shiloh kept her face carefully even, but
something flickered in her green eyes.

"No." Con shook his head. "Not Sam. Not in a million
years."

She raised an eyebrow at him. He looked away, staring
out to sea. He knew she had guessed that the thought had
occurred to him before, or the denial wouldn't have been so
close to the surface.

"Con," she began.

He turned his head back to her. "It can't be. I know he's got to be high up, to have the kind of access he must have, but not Sam. It can't be."

She heard the undertone of desperation in his voice and could see its echo in a pair of blue eyes lit by silver moonlight. She saw then that there was much more involved here than just the security of a company. At stake was some deeply buried part of the man beside her, the one battered part of his soul that clung to some tiny bit of faith in his fellow man. If his joker indeed turned out to be the very man who had sent him here, that faith, and most likely that soul, would be destroyed.

"All right."

He had to be right, she thought. She couldn't bear to see what it would do to him if he were wrong.

Satisfied that the anchor was set and the natural circle the boat would prescribe as the wind shifted would still be clear of the rocks, Shiloh walked back to the cockpit from the bow.

They had rounded the southern tip of Catalina Island at a safe distance. The high, barren bluffs of the south end looked starkly white against the night sky, and they could hear the wash of the surf as it hit the rugged shoreline.

This was her favorite cove on the windward side of the island. It was sheltered, the water was crystal clear, and there was a lovely little crescent of beach ashore. She was delighted to have found it empty; it made anchoring much easier, because there were no other boats to contend with, and she knew it well enough to be able to do it in darkness.

Con had been silent since that brief discussion about Sam. He stared out into the darkness, away from the wide path of moonlight, as if he needed the blackness to mask his thoughts. She had seen first her father, then her brother, wrestle with doubts too many times to interrupt with any banal platitudes. She merely gave him directions to help with the anchoring.

"Seven to one," she told him. "Pay out seven times the depth." He had followed her instructions exactly. And silently.

When they were set, she went below and made coffee, and he took the cup she offered with a nod and a short "thank you." Then he slipped back into silence, and she left him to it. She stretched out on the cockpit seat, savoring the sound of the water and giving quiet thanks for the too often taken for granted California climate that allowed her to sit there quite comfortably in only a heavy sweatshirt in the middle of October.

They watched the world grow light around them, although the little cove, nestled below the bulk and height of the island, remained in shadow. What mist there was cleared at the first touch of the sun, and Shiloh knew they were going to have one of those beautiful, bright fall days.

She sighed with pleasure, stretching luxuriously as she drew a deep breath of salt-tangy air. She sensed Con's gaze on her and looked over to find him watching her intently.

"It's going to be beautiful," she said, her voice soft, still under the spell of the glorious dawn.

"Yes." His eyes never left her.

"I . . . I'm going to go for a swim and a wash." She wondered why she felt so breathless. "I usually just use the fresh water in the tank to rinse off. There should be some biodegradable soap in the head. There's plenty of water for a shower, though, if you want." Why was she rambling like this?

Great, Con thought. A dawn swim in paradise. Wearing what? Or, more importantly, not wearing what? His stomach knotted. Hastily he spoke.

"How much water is there?"

"She carries 170 gallons, and she's full. We can always go around to Avalon if we need anything, but if we're aiming for complete isolation, we've got enough for almost a month if we're careful, two weeks if we're not."

"Oh."

He felt a strange weakness in his knees that told him if he'd been standing, it wouldn't have been for long. An image of an endless stretch of days on this elegant little vessel, alone with her, away from the outside world that had once again turned sour on him, turned his muscles to mush and his insides to rock.

"How much time are we going to need?"

He shook off the vision. "Not that much." When she looked at him with those delicate brows just barely furrowed, he realized that his voice had held an undertone of disappointment. He tried again. "Sam will be back in two days. I'll give him the name, then the decision is his."

Whatever doubts he'd had, he'd conquered them now. Or buried them, she thought. There was nothing in his voice but businesslike precision.

"And if they find us?"

His mouth twisted wryly. "I'll wish this thing had a cannon."

She started to laugh, then stopped. "It just might," she said, and disappeared below. Curious, he followed, watching her pull open the teak door to one of the larger lockers. She reached inside and came out with a spotless, well-oiled, pump-action shotgun. She handed it to him.

"Wayne doesn't always sail the friendly seas," she explained at his look, then reached back into the locker.

Great, he thought as he hefted the weapon. Wayne again. Why did he have to be so damned efficient? And why did she know where every damned thing on this boat was?

Shiloh handed him the box of shells she'd found. "I don't imagine he keeps it loaded in port," she said, wondering at his rather fierce expression.

He pumped it once and found she was right. He took five of the .00 shells and loaded it, pumping one round into the chamber.

"You ever use one of these?" He was almost surprised when she shook her head no. Then he turned and propped it near the main hatch, where it could be reached easily. "Don't forget it's primed and ready," he said as he turned back to her. He reached behind him, pulling her .45 out of the small of his back. He held it out to her.

"Thank you."

"I said you'd get it back."

"Do you always keep your promises?"

"Yes. That's why I don't make many." He abruptly turned his back on her and put the box of shells next to the gun.

Whew, Shiloh thought. I feel like I've just been warned off. In the next minute she was laughing at herself for reading anything personal into his words or his manner. He was in the middle of a tempest; the last thing he would be thinking about was her. Besides, he didn't know the odd things that had been happening to her every time she looked at him.

And a good thing, too, she chided herself. Even if it is his own fault. If her first sight of him hadn't been nearly naked across her bed, her mind wouldn't be traveling in these uncalled for directions. Not to mention the sight of him sprawled naked on her living room floor.

She felt that irritating heat rise to her face once more, and she glanced at him to be sure he wasn't looking. It was a mistake, because in that first instant of looking at his lean, muscular body, she could picture it as clearly as if the tight jeans and soft blue sweater didn't exist. She looked away hurriedly.

She pulled open the drawer beneath the forward double bunk and dug around in it for a moment. She found a pale green one-piece bathing suit that looked like it might fit and took it out. When she straightened up, Con was there, his expression oddly tense.

"Yours?"

His eyes were on the suit. His relief that she didn't have some notion about skinny-dipping in this secluded spot was marred by a niggling little regret over the same thing. At least it wasn't some skimpy little bikini, he thought. That would be too much for his already strained control.

"No," she said, puzzled. "Wayne keeps several here for guests. There's probably one you can use, too."

Wayne. He was beginning to hate the name. And the man, sight unseen. "Wayne must be quite a guy."

"He is. I admire him a lot."

"I can see that. So why don't you admire him into your voyage around the world on this tub?" His tone made it impossible to mistake his meaning.

"She's not a tub! And Wayne is a sweet, kind man who just happens to be old enough to be my grandfather, and I don't appreciate your rotten insinuations!"

She slammed the drawer shut and pushed past him into the head, the door slamming behind her even more loudly. She stripped off her jeans and the bloody sweatshirt, then the rest, kicking her deck shoes aside angrily. She yanked on the green suit and looked into the mirror, which was surprisingly large for the small space.

It would have to do, she thought, although it was a little skimpy on top for someone as generously endowed as she was. And the French-cut legs were awfully high.... It doesn't matter, she told herself. No one's going to see you except one bad-tempered, dirty-minded private spy. Who seems to have the knack of destroying your control. She grabbed a towel and the soap, then gathered up her clothes and shoes and dumped them on the bunk as she passed.

Con was pacing in the spacious cockpit, mentally kicking himself. What the hell was he doing, mouthing off like that? She'd done nothing but help him—risked her life for him, in fact, not to mention coming up with probably the best way to truly lose those gorillas who were on his tail. And what had it gotten her? The sour side of his tongue, that's what.

And why? He shied away from the question of why the thought of the unknown Wayne had bothered him so much. And why finding out the truth about him had been such a relief.

He owed her an apology, that was certain. Again. He chuckled mirthlessly. He wasn't sure an apology would be enough, this time. Maybe if he groveled, he thought ruefully. Maybe if he—

He broke off, swallowing heavily. Oh, Lord. And he had been stupid enough to be grateful it hadn't been a bikini, he thought numbly as she came up through the hatch like Venus rising. All that was missing was the dolphins.

She didn't even look at him as she walked toward the back of the cockpit, her lingering anger clear in her stiff posture. He gaped at her, unable to tear his eyes away from the slender yet lusciously curved figure bared to his gaze. The high cut of the suit made her legs look impossibly long, golden and beautifully shaped, and his throat tightened as his heart began to pound.

He forced his eyes upward over the gentle swell of her hips and the inward curve of her slim waist, only to have them stop with arresting suddenness on the curves of her breasts, full and lush beneath the shimmering mint fabric that had to strain to contain them.

His jeans were suddenly experiencing much the same problem. He couldn't seem to stop the sudden images that leapt to his mind, those long, incredible legs wrapped around him, his hand peeling away that thin layer of green to let her breasts spill free, bare for his hands, his mouth....

She was past him now, but the taut, trim curve of her buttocks gave him no relief. He leaned against the cabin roof weakly. He couldn't fight this. He didn't know how anymore, it had been so long. Or had it ever been like this? Had he ever felt anything so fierce, so fast?

She draped the towel she held over the rail, and lifted one small foot to the cockpit seat. "Sh—Shiloh?"

He sounded as if he'd been punched in the stomach. She looked back over one slender shoulder at him, the shining green of the swimsuit making her eyes come alive. He turned slightly, away from her, uncomfortably aware of the aching tightness of his body.

"I..." He had to stop and take a deep breath to steady himself. She waited. Silently. "I was out of line. I don't have any excuse for it. I just...I haven't..." He swore under his breath. "I've forgotten how to just talk to people. How to look at them like human beings, not tools."

Her foot came back to the deck. She turned to face him.

He tried to keep his voice even as he struggled to control his rebellious body. "I never meant to treat you like that. You, of all people." He took one more breath. "I'm sorry.

Again. Still." He gave a shaky little laugh. "Maybe I should just apologize for my next stupid move now. Save time."

"Apologize twice," she said, straight-faced. "That'll hold you for a couple of days."

He stared at her for a moment, uncertain. Then he caught the glitter in her eyes and the barest twitch at the corners of her soft mouth.

"How about three times? I like to stay ahead."

The twitch won, and she smiled. "Consider yourself paid-up in advance."

He studied the teak deck beneath his feet. "You're pretty generous." *You wouldn't be if you knew what I'd been thinking,* he muttered to himself.

"Generous enough to share the Pacific, even. I'll wait, if you want to swim." He hesitated. "Just forget it for a while, Con. It's a beautiful day, and a beautiful place. If they find us, we'll handle it then, but for now, can you just enjoy it?"

Could he? Just relax and enjoy, with no thought of what had been, or what might come? Or had he lost the knack completely? A beautiful day and a beautiful place. And a very beautiful woman. A woman who turned him inside out like no one ever had, just by her presence.

Suddenly, even knowing he was asking for trouble, he wanted to do as she asked more than anything in the world. He wanted to steal this moment out of time, to have this one brilliant day to stack against all the dark, ugly ones. *I can handle it,* he told himself. *She was Linc's little sister, for God's sake. Surely that would keep his recalcitrant body in line. Just keep remembering that,* he told himself as he went to dig in the drawer that had produced that incredible slash of pastel green.

After discarding a minimal racing suit and a pair of trunks that would have fit any member of the local whale population, he found a pair of nylon running shorts that fit and could double for trunks. He changed quickly, tossing his rather the worse for wear clothes on the bunk beside hers. And refusing resolutely to notice that the bunk was huge, at least the size of her bed.

The moment he reappeared on deck she was up on the rail, swinging those long, golden legs over the stainless steel stern pulpit.

''Race you to the beach!'' she called, then was gone in a flash of shimmering green and bare skin.

For a second he just watched, thinking how like her it was just to plunge in; no one-toe-at-a-time testing the waters for Shiloh Reese. She was cutting through the ocean cleanly, with an effortless stroke that spoke of a long familiarity with the water. Then he went after her, gasping a little at the shock of the cold water; fall might not have hit the air yet, but the ocean knew it was here.

She beat him handily and was standing on the deserted little beach, wringing water out of her hair, when he got to his feet and waded the rest of the way in. She was laughing exuberantly, her eyes sparkling.

He couldn't take his eyes off her as he sloshed through the surf toward her. She leaned back to squeeze the last drops of seawater from her hair, bending her supple body easily. Her nipples were taut from the chill and pressed against the wet fabric as her breasts were thrust upward by the movement.

Easy, McQuade, he ordered, tearing his gaze from her. You've got nowhere to hide in these wet shorts. Linc's little sister. Remember that. It would work. It had to work. Except that right now she didn't look like anyone's little sister.

They explored the little cove as far as they could in bare feet, then came back to sit on the sand as the morning sun cleared the island and hit the little beach. There was a tense moment when another boat came into view, but it appeared set on a course and continued with only a wave from the gray-haired man at the wheel and his plump wife.

Gradually, as the sun warmed his skin and took away the chill, Con dropped back in the sand. He consciously let his taut muscles relax, amazed at how the tension seemed to flow out of him as if it were a liquid thing. It felt good to just lie there lazily, pretending for the moment that he hadn't a care in the world.

"Con?"

"Mmm."

"What's this from?"

It took every ounce of self-control he possessed not to jump upright when he felt her fingertips brush over his chest. He kept his eyes closed, not daring to look at her as she traced the path of that old mark, making it flame as if it were fresh. It was a moment after her fingers left him before he could trust himself to answer.

"A knife." He looked up at her from under half-lowered lids, saw white, even teeth bite at her full, lower lip, saw the furrow between her brows. "I never said I was pretty," he said, a little tightly.

"You don't have to say it."

His eyes snapped completely open at that. She looked away quickly, but not before he'd seen the two spots of pink that colored her cheeks. Warmth flooded him, and his heart began to race.

"I'll race you back." She sounded as breathless as if she already had. "I'm hungry."

He beat her easily this time, but Shiloh wasn't concentrating on her swimming. She kept running her thumb over the tips of her fingers, wondering why they were still tingling, as they had when she had first reached out to touch him. She couldn't believe the feel of him, sleek and smooth skin over hard muscle. She had wanted to go on, beyond the thin, white scar, to run her fingertips down his breastbone, over the taut muscles, to his flat, male nipples. . . .

She was glad then for the water's chill. She didn't understand what was happening to her. She'd never felt like this before, never felt so much from so little, never felt so driven for more. She found most of the men she met boring, wrapped up in their shallow little worlds that had so little to do with reality. Even Jimmy, whom she liked a great deal, was at a loss if it didn't deal with sailing or Mandy.

Wayne was different, and she'd secretly agreed with him when he'd laughingly joked about wishing he was fifty years younger for her. She adored him, and not just because he was a sort of benevolent adopted uncle. He was the kind of man she'd been afraid didn't exist anymore.

Or was it her? Had she made a trade-off, the price for her hard-won control the surrender of whatever it was that had attracted man after man to women like her mother? She'd always laughed it off, saying she wanted nothing to do with that kind of man anyway, but lately she'd been wondering if there was any other kind. She had her brother and her father as proof that there were, but she'd been beginning to think they were the last of the breed.

Until now.

He was waiting for her at the boat and tossed her the soap she'd left on the cockpit seat. They took turns using it, by tacit mutual consent giving each other privacy, never guessing it was for the same reason; neither of them could quite handle the sight of slick, soapy hands sliding over temptingly bare skin.

It took her a little longer, and when she was done she clambered up over the rail and reached for her towel. Con was lifting the seats, peering into the big lockers beneath them. He'd been too preoccupied to do much exploring before, but he was curious now. Shiloh watched him, watched the muscles flex beneath the slick, smooth skin, marveling at how the scars that marked him only emphasized the sleek perfection of the rest. The wet shorts clung to him tantalizingly, and she buried her face in the towel to mask her own astonishment at how her pulse began to speed up.

When she had regained her composure she hung her towel over the pulpit next to his and went below. Con followed her, poking into the various shelves and cubbies with interest, remarking on how well-organized everything was, and how suited to the sea.

"It's gimballed," she said in answer to the tenth question he asked, this one about the big table in the main salon. "Just like the stove. It swings to stay horizontal when the boat shifts or heels over."

He made her take him through the whole vessel, pointing at everything and asking what seemed like a hundred questions. Since it was her favorite subject, and he seemed genuinely interested rather than just killing time, she didn't mind and answered as thoroughly as she could.

Finally, however, over her growling stomach, she laughingly begged for mercy. "I'll even cook," she pleaded. "Go ahead and rinse off." And get dressed, she added silently. Please get dressed. Those damned shorts are more than I can take.

"I don't know," he said, holding up his clothes rather gingerly. "These have had a rough day and night."

She snapped her fingers, remembering. She lifted her nylon suitcase up to the bunk and unzipped it. Digging into it, she pulled out a pair of jeans and a striped rugby shirt. "Here."

He looked at her blankly.

"They're Linc's. I thought you might need something. You're about the same size."

He shook his head in wonder. "You never miss a trick, do you?"

"Sure I do, but the *Phoenix* doesn't. She even has a washing machine." He stared at her in disbelief. She pulled open the cupboard he'd been standing in front of, about the only one they hadn't gotten to. He stared at the tiny but very efficient looking washer. And below it, incredibly, a small dryer. "Comes in handy when nothing will dry outside."

"Maybe you *could* go around the world," he muttered as he tried the richly tiled shower and found it complete with scalding hot water. He turned down the H tap and upped the C. Stripping off the nylon shorts and hanging them under the stream of fresh water, he rinsed off quickly, trying not to think of the woman who would soon be in here, as naked as he was now. Swiftly he rinsed the saltwater from his hair and shut off the water.

He dried himself on a new towel, beginning to realize that a dryer on a boat wasn't as absurd as it sounded. No, this was quite a little ship, he thought as he pulled on the clothes she'd packed for him. And she was...Linc's little sister. Maybe it would be easier to remember if he was wearing Linc's clothes. Somehow he doubted it.

Chapter 7

He couldn't remember a day like this one. He couldn't remember if he'd ever even had one. They ate, lounged in the fall sunshine, ate some more, lounged some more. She tried to teach him about all the rigging on the boat, amid laughter over his comments about the absurdity of the terminology.

"It's a rope. Why don't you call it that?"

"Because it's a sheet."

"That's dumb. If anything on this boat should be a sheet, it would be the sail."

It went on, both of them getting sillier and sillier, until Con stopped, staring at her in what appeared to be awe. He'd never in his life engaged in this kind of laughable inanity, not even as a child. Especially not as a child. He wasn't quite sure how to deal with it now.

"Are you all right?" She was looking at him with her head cocked to one side.

"I . . . Fine. What do you want for dinner? I'll cook, if you're feeling brave."

It wasn't nearly as risky as he'd implied; the cupboards yielded a can of salmon with a recipe that produced a more than passable salmon loaf. He felt ridiculously proud as it quickly disappeared.

Shiloh had found a full bottle of wine to go with it, but Con discreetly limited himself to one glass. Although he had managed to do as she had asked to a great extent and put the hovering threat out of his mind, he wasn't able to forget it to the point of letting himself get drunk.

It was as she picked up the glass he'd refilled for her a second time that Shiloh realized it. "Just so far and no further," she murmured. He didn't pretend not to understand.

"It's the best I can do."

She raised her glass. "It's better than I expected."

He grinned. "Is that an insult or a compliment?"

"A compliment. You didn't have to apologize all day."

"Does that mean I've got another day paid in advance?"

"Sure. I'm feeling generous. It was a wonderful day."

"It was." His voice was serious now. "I've never had a day like this."

For some reason Shiloh found herself thinking of the moment when she'd told him Linc had envied him, and of his astonished response. Just the fact that he was so amazed that anyone would envy him, and that the simple pleasure of a day like today was so foreign to him, told her worlds about the life he'd lived.

"Never?"

He recoiled inwardly from the soft, warm sympathy in her voice. He didn't know why it was so important; he only knew the last thing he wanted from her was pity. And the first thing he wanted from her? The first thing would have her brother calling you out at dawn for pistols at twenty paces, he thought sourly. And Lincoln Reese just might be the man who could beat him.

"Nope," he said flippantly, looking away from her as he rubbed a hand over his now stubble-free jaw; the worthy Wayne indeed kept a razor aboard. "There aren't a lot of sailboats in Denver."

She didn't react to his tone. "You grew up in Denver?"

"Sort of." His voice had gone flat, expressionless.

Shiloh knew he had suddenly tensed, but she couldn't seem to stop herself. "Is your family still there?" The question slipped out before she remembered that he'd said there was no one. No levers to use on him.

"What the hell is this, an inquisition?" He erupted into motion, getting to his feet in one swift, barely controlled movement.

"Only when *I* ask, apparently," she answered, stung.

He lowered his eyes as if abashed, but his jaw was still rigidly set. Without a word he turned, climbed out of the cockpit and strode toward the bow.

Shiloh watched him go with a twinge of guilt. She should have remembered what he'd said. What was it about him that made her forget herself so? She got angry at the drop of a hat, and turned to jelly just as quickly. It seemed she was either snapping at him or her voice went all soft and husky. She hated the first, and the second seemed to make him turn on her.

Her hard-won, much vaunted calm had become a thing of the past, and she couldn't seem to get it back. Where she had always analyzed, considered, pondered, with him she just reacted. Since he had appeared in her life she had regressed to some emotional, instinctive creature she didn't recognize.

She looked at him, a dark, brooding silhouette against a sky rapidly building to the glorious oranges, pinks and purples of a California sunset. A solitary, isolated figure. In that moment she saw the essence of his life, solitary by chance, isolated by choice. Necessary choice.

In idle moments, when she had considered in her analytical way the grim possibilities of losing her father or her brother to the hazards of their work, she had wondered which would be worse, to have no one give a damn about you or no one to give a damn about. She had never thought about the horror of both together. A horror he lived with every day. She was filled with remorse at having brought it up, at having reminded him, even though she wasn't certain of what.

She knew better than to approach him, to apologize; the stiff set of his neck and shoulders told her that. With a sigh she went below. Feeling the need to do something, to channel that urge to go to him into some kind of motion, she pulled on the green swimsuit again.

It was still damp and felt uncomfortably clammy on her skin, but she ignored it. She picked up a towel that was also slightly damp but would serve for wiping away the seawater and went back to the cockpit.

Con hadn't moved except to lift one hand to grip the forestay as he stood out on the bowsprit. Once more she felt a strong pull to go to him, a pull so strong it frightened her a little. The sight of him, so alone as he stared out at the empty sea, tore at her in a way she'd never felt before. She backed up, as if by putting more distance between them she could lessen the power of the attraction. It didn't work.

The boat had swung sideways to the small beach, so she sat on the port rail and quickly swung her legs over. The water was a cold shock as she slipped in, and she began to swim immediately to ward off the chill.

The air seemed warm by comparison as she walked onto the sand, staying in the shelter of a jagged outcropping of rock, using it as a windbreak. She sat down, using the base of the rock as a backrest while she watched the sun as it made its plunge for the horizon. It was only then that she noticed the lone figure was gone from the bow of the boat.

A movement near the cockpit caught her eye, and she shifted her glance in time to see a lean, muscled body arc in a smooth, powerful dive, breaking the water with barely a ripple. She watched that dark head approach her as he cut through the water with long, rhythmic strokes, watched with fascination, as she had not been able to before.

When he rose from the water, he seemed to hesitate for a moment, looking at her. Shiloh returned the look, unable to tear her eyes away from the muscled sleekness of him, the wedge of broad shoulders to narrow hips, the flat ridges of his belly, the long, leanly muscled legs. Again her imagination supplied the details the clinging, wet nylon barely hid, and again she felt that flush of heat flood her.

Why? She'd seen men better-looking than he was; California was full of them. Better-looking and without that haunted look, that sense of being driven, that air of having walked too long on the dark side. None of them had had this effect on her. Why was it he alone who stirred this fire in her?

He began to move then, as if her gaze had been a signal. She wondered what he would have done if she had looked away, had turned from him. Would he still have come to her, or would he have gone back as he had come, a lone figure slicing through a sunset sea? Of course he would have gone, she told herself severely, trying not to notice how much the thought stung.

He was there now, dropping down to sit beside her. Without a word she moved over to let him share her backrest. His eyes never left her. The silence spun out as he searched her face. The image of that solitary figure came back to her as if she could see it in the blue depths of his eyes.

"I'm sorry—" They said it in unison, then stopped, laughing awkwardly. After a moment he spoke again.

"I shouldn't have gotten mad at you. Or yelled at you. Or sworn at you. I'm sorry."

"You don't have to apologize. You paid in advance, remember?"

Con was amazed at the strength of the relief that filled him. "I used them all up in a hurry, didn't I?"

"Not all. I owe you one, too. I was prying. I'm sorry."

He sucked in a deep breath, and Shiloh could almost feel the effort he made to relax the instinctive tightening of his jaw. "No. You weren't. You were just asking a simple question. I'm the one who went haywire."

"Why?"

His breath came out in a long sigh as his head lolled back to rest on the ledge of rock behind them. "I...I'm not used to..." He drew another breath, then tried again. "I don't know how to... If somebody asks me about myself, I tell them whatever I think will get what I need from them. Whatever will make them trust me, or fear me, or whatever it takes to get them to tell me what I need to know, or to make that slip that gives me what I want.''

''It's part of the job.'' Her words were accepting, understanding. She'd heard Linc and her father talk too many times about that part of it, the part they hated most, the using. ''But you're not working now.''

He laughed, a harsh, grating sound. ''I'm not? Am I ever not? I don't think I know how to stop anymore.''

''So why didn't you just . . . make up something?''

Why hadn't he? He lifted his head to look at her. ''I don't know.'' He shrugged one shoulder, trying to belie his own uncertainty.

The question had suddenly become important to Shiloh. Very important, for reasons she didn't understand. ''I would have believed you,'' she began.

That harsh chuckle came again. ''Maybe that's why I didn't.'' He met her gaze then. ''No,'' he said slowly, painfully. ''I just didn't want to lie to you.''

At his barely perceptible emphasis on the ''you,'' Shiloh's heart skipped a beat, then raced to catch up.

''Then why not tell me the truth?''

''God, I'm not sure I know how anymore.'' The words came out in a sudden burst, as if against his will. He recovered quickly, going back to that flippant tone to cover the break. ''The truth's not very interesting, anyway.''

She studied him for a moment. ''Is it really that hard?''

He opened his mouth, another insouciant remark on the tip of his tongue. But something in her gaze, something warm and sweet and innocent, stopped him. He lowered his eyes.

''Yes.'' It was barely audible.

Somehow she knew how much even that small admission had cost him. She wanted to reach out to him, to hold him, to comfort him, but she didn't dare; just looking at him did such crazy things to her. Just looking at the dark sweep of his lowered lashes, the way his wet, dark hair clung to the back of his neck, the way the firm line of his jaw blended into the masculine cords of his neck, the way the pulse beat in the hollow of his throat . . .

She felt that glowing heat inside her send up a little tongue of flame, and she searched for something to say.

"Linc always said that when it got harder to tell the truth than to lie, it was time for a vacation."

His head shot up, his eyes fastening on hers. With the slowness of a sunrise, a rueful smile curved his mouth. "That brother of yours is too damned smart for his own good."

Shiloh smiled, both at the change in his expression and the open affection in his tone. "Runs in the family," she quipped, and was rewarded with a grin. "So," she went on after a moment, "shall we consider this a vacation?"

"From what?"

"Everything. Including questions."

He couldn't quite believe she was going to let him off the hook. He shifted, turning so that he faced her, barely a foot away. "Just like that?"

She smiled at his words, and her voice was soft. "Just like that."

Con shook his head in wonder. He stared at her, at those green eyes glowing with the last rays of the sun, at the thick, spiky points of lashes still wet from her swim and the sassy, uptilted nose.

Slowly his hand rose, as if against his own volition. His fingers went to cup her cheek, while his thumb gently brushed away the glistening drops. He swallowed heavily at the feel of her silken skin, and his heart began to pound when she tilted her head, not to get away but to get closer to his hand.

Shiloh had lost any awareness of what she was doing at the first touch of his fingers on her face. She felt suddenly chilled because of the heat that leapt beneath his touch. She couldn't seem to get enough air, and her lips parted as she tried to breathe faster.

With exquisite slowness his thumb slid downward to run lightly over her mouth, outlining first the delicately shaped upper lip, then lingering on the fullness of the lower. That single tongue of flame that had flared in her as he had walked up the beach toward her erupted into a blaze, spreading the heat throughout her suddenly trembling body.

Con was beyond caring that he was out of line, beyond wondering what the hell he was doing, beyond worrying that his body's reaction to merely touching her was unmistakable. He only knew that in this moment, despite all his considerable will and resolve, he was going to kiss her. He had to kiss her, as surely as he had to take his next breath.

Had she made one sound of protest, he might have been able to stop, but she only tilted her head back, as if offering her mouth. He took it fiercely, but gentled instantly at the first stiffening of her muscles. His hands slipped up to the back of her head, fingers threading through her slick, wet hair as he cradled her, exerting only the slightest pressure to press her lips to his.

He could taste the salt from the sea lingering on the softness of her mouth, but the sweetness soon overwhelmed it. He felt her lips go warm and pliant beneath his, and his blood began to hammer in his ears. His hands tightened convulsively behind her head.

Shiloh couldn't believe what was happening to her. She'd been kissed before, but never had it felt like this. Never had she flared into such an inferno; never had she been so swiftly hungry for more. His lips were hot and fierce, yet gentle and coaxing, and they were turning her to molten, flowing liquid in his hands.

His mouth was moving on hers, asking, wanting. When she felt the tip of his tongue brush her lips, they parted for him naturally; to refuse him never occurred to her whirling, spinning brain. It had been numbed by his first touch, surrendering all control to her newly awakened, sizzling senses.

She wasn't aware she had moved until her fingers felt the damp thickness of the hair at the nape of his neck. The moment her hands locked behind his neck he moved, twisting sideways to pull her down beside him on the sand. Never breaking the kiss, he stretched out next to her, throwing one leg over hers as if he were afraid she would escape.

He *was* afraid. She had singed him just as that sweet dream had, and he was afraid she would somehow dissolve into that disappearing figure again. Not yet, he pleaded silently. He hadn't had enough yet. He might never have enough. He was drinking in the soft sweetness of her like dusty earth after a ten-year drought.

His tongue crept deeper, flickering over her lips, tracing the even line of her teeth. She made a quiet little sound and then, tentatively, almost shyly, her tongue met his, brushing it with the barest of touches before retreating. An electric little shock raced through him at the touch, but it was that trace of innocent shyness that brought reality caving in on him.

He froze, suddenly aware that he had pinned her to the sand beneath them, that his body was pulsing, throbbing, with need too long denied, and that the evidence of that need was pressed tightly against her hip. She was looking up at him with eyes that were wide and dreamy, and her face was flushed from his kiss. She looked amazed and yet full of an ancient feminine wisdom, both innocent and seductive, and the impossible contrast only made his body clench tighter as another piercing shaft of desire stabbed him.

A different kind of color rose in her cheeks as he stared down at her, and the dreamy, distant look faded as she came back from the fiery world he had sent her to. The worldliness and seductiveness vanished, leaving only the amazed innocence.

What did you expect? Con swore viciously at himself as he wrenched himself off her. That she was the kind of woman accustomed to being attacked on a deserted beach by a man she barely knew? He felt every one of his thirty-four years, and felt the dinginess of those years even more. His stomach knotted with a fierce self-contempt, as if he had soiled something clean and pure and beautiful. He had already dragged her down into the muck he lived in; wasn't that enough?

He drew his knees up in front of him, circling his arms around them, trying to both hide and ignore the surging, aching hardness of his body. He stared out at the last little crescent of the sun that was about to slide out of sight, silently berating himself.

Shiloh was still quivering in reaction. Her lips still tingled, and the tip of her tongue crept out to touch them, as if she could still taste him there. Gradually the flowing heat ebbed to be replaced by a growing, gnawing doubt.

She sat up, shivering a little as she methodically brushed the sand from her arms, her legs. On the edge of her vision was that huddled figure, as alone now as he had been on the bow of the boat. Her mind was racing. Had she done something, made some unconscious sound or movement, that had caused that sudden, chilling withdrawal? She didn't know. She brushed at more sand.

It wasn't working, Con thought. He was as hard and tight and aching as he had been when he'd rolled away from her. From the corner of his eye he could still see her, could see the graceful movements of her slender hands and arms as she brushed away the sand, could see the golden length of her legs. Now that he had tasted the sweetness of her mouth, had found out what incredible things it did to him, anything more didn't bear thinking about.

He'd left it too long, that was all. He should have taken that redhead in New York up on her offer three months ago. Or the blonde in Houston last year. That he hadn't had the slightest desire to make love with either one of them, or any of several before them, was no comfort now.

That's all it is, he repeated silently. Even though it had been, in a way, by choice, he'd been celibate for too long, and his body had just picked now to remind him. Right, McQuade, he muttered silently to himself. You just keep telling yourself that.

He had to do something, he thought desperately. He had to stop this pulsing ache before he reached for her; he had no illusions about his ability to stop again. Keeping his back carefully to her, he stood up. He muttered something about the boat, and without looking at her, he headed for the water.

He nearly gasped aloud at the shock of the October ocean against his heated skin; the Pacific had suddenly become the

Antarctic. Good, he thought grimly, and struck out for the *Phoenix* with his longest, fastest stroke. He stretched out, pushing himself to the utmost, needing the strain of exertion to divert his raging body. By the time he reached the boat he was cooler, if not relaxed, and his aching flesh seemed to have gotten the message. He took the towel she'd laid out and dried off, then went to get her another to replace it. When he came back she was there, climbing over the rail, and he held it out to her silently.

She took it with a nod, wiping off minimally before she disappeared below. He heard the door to the head close and the shower start. A vision of her peeling off the wisp of swimsuit flashed through his mind before he slammed the door once more on thoughts of that kind.

Later, as he lay awake in the aft bunk he'd gone to the moment she'd climbed into the forward one, he wondered why he was even trying to go to sleep. It had been a strained evening until a leaping fish had broken the water, startling them both, and breaking the tension, as well. They'd been able to talk after that, although the memory of that searing kiss hung between them like Damocles' sword.

Why her? he asked himself for the hundredth time. Why her and not any of the others who had happened along over the last couple of years? Cissy, the blonde from Houston, hadn't affected him at all, even though she was a classic beauty in the way Shiloh would never be, not with that up-turned nose and defiant chin.

He smiled in the darkness as he thought of those two sassy features, but the smile faded when the memory of her mouth followed close behind. He rolled over to face the teak-lined hull, drawing his knees up in an involuntary movement as the ache began again. It was a long, long time before he slept.

Shiloh sat up in her bunk, unsure of what had awakened her, knowing only that she hadn't slept long enough. Of course, lying awake for hours hadn't helped, but, as with everything else, her control over her mind and an imagination that had become unusually vivid had seemed nonexistent.

She had relived those moments on the beach time after time before she had at last drifted off to sleep, only to relive them even more clearly in her dreams. She had racked her brain for something she might have done, something wrong, something that had made him pull away like that. She couldn't find anything, unless her inexperience had been so painfully obvious that he found it repellent.

And if he hadn't? She had asked herself that question over and over, as well. What would she have done if he hadn't stopped? Would she have halted him, presuming she could have, or would she have let her senses, and the way he brought them cracklingly to life, carry her away?

"Oh, God," she moaned, wrapping her arms around herself. There had been a time when she would have scoffed at the idea of losing control like that. She couldn't scoff any longer. The thought of making love with him there on the beach, or anywhere else, sent little ripples of flame along nerves that had never truly been used before, and the shock of it swept through every inch of her body.

But now, staring at the moonlit sea through the small porthole, she made herself face the truth. She would not have stopped him, not when his fingers merely brushing her cheek set her on fire, not when his mouth on hers made her feel that way, not when the feel of his aroused body pressing against her made her ache so fiercely in some hot, swirling place she'd never known existed deep inside her.

He had wanted her. She might be naive, but she could hardly not have noticed. Or was she too naive? Had he not wanted her, but just . . . wanted? Her cheeks flamed once more.

When the sound came, she knew as soon as she heard it that it was what had awakened her. A small, nondescript sound, low and barely audible. She froze, listening, but heard nothing other than the pounding of her heart.

After a moment she swung her bare legs over the edge of the bunk and hopped down to the teak planking. She tugged at the sweatshirt she'd washed that afternoon and put on to sleep in, pulling it down where it had been pushed up to her waist in her restless sleep. Quietly she padded toward the sound. She paused as she passed the galley, listening once more. Still nothing. She hesitated. If it had been only Con, she would wind up embarrassing them both. But if not . . . She made herself move.

She checked the main hatchway and found it locked and secure, as they had left it. She hesitated again. She was barely three feet from Con's cabin; she could just peek around the corner and make sure he was all right, that he hadn't become ill again.

He was asleep. A sleep as restless as hers had been, judging from the tangle of covers. Her throat tightened as her eyes followed the edge of the blankets as they slanted down across his chest, belly and legs, baring his right side to her and leaving her no doubts that he was naked. The only break in that sleek expanse of skin was the puckered ridge of the scar marking the wound that had started him on a long, hard road.

With a sudden rush of tenderness and longing that startled her, she wished she could have known him then, before that bullet had destroyed what innocence he might have had. She wished she could have known the boy he'd been; maybe it would help her to understand the man he'd become.

He stirred, and she hastily backed up a step, flushing with embarrassment at just the thought of being caught watching him. She turned to go.

"No."

She nearly ran; there was no mistaking that the sound had come from him. Only the recognition that it was the same sound that had awakened her stopped her.

"No."

His head tossed on the pillow as the single word came again. A low, mumbled protest, a harsh, whispered syllable made ominous by its very quietness.

She couldn't just walk away and leave him in the grips of what was clearly a nightmare, no matter what her common sense might tell her. Taking a deep breath and steeling herself, she stepped through the small doorway and across to the bunk. She wetted her lips to say his name, but her throat was oddly dry. She reached out to gently shake him.

She had forgotten what had happened the last time.

Chapter 8

Before she had time to think, she was wedged between him and the hull of the boat, her wrist once more in that iron grip that she had felt for hours after the first time he'd tossed her. This time his reaction was immediate; he released her and backed away. But there was no apology this time, just the steady, burning gaze of blue eyes that were unreadable in the dim light.

She'd been startled this time, but not frightened; in fact, she felt a little foolish for having fallen victim to his lightning reflexes twice. She tried to speak, to make light of it, but her mouth had become as dry as her throat under that unrelenting stare. Unconsciously, her tongue crept out to wet her lips.

"Oh, God."

Con gave a low, husky groan and reached out to pull her to him. All his hours of self-lecturing went up in smoke at the first taste of her lips; all his resolve disintegrated in the first second he felt her begin to yield to him. After the first startled moment she went soft and warm, and he pulled her closer.

He should be angry, he thought. Angry at her for coming to him like this, angry at himself for not being able to resist the temptation. And angry at the fates that had thrown him together with the one woman in the world he'd ever met who could do this to him without even trying. Could do this to him by just...being.

But anger was the last thing he was feeling. His senses were too full of the soft sweetness of her, his every nerve sizzlingly aware of the feel of her body pressed to his. It was just a kiss, he told himself. Just a kiss? How could just a simple kiss be so sweet, so painfully sweet?

And then it wasn't a simple kiss anymore. He took her mouth hungrily, urgently, all the smothered need boiling to the surface. He plunged his tongue into her honeyed warmth, unaware of the low sound he made when her tongue danced up to tangle with his, eagerly this time. Her hands were at his nape, her slender fingers tangling in the thick, dark hair, pulling him closer.

Shiloh had never known she could feel a kiss in so many places. This one sent fire racing to the outer limits of her body, then returned it to settle in that deep, secret, newly discovered place in the pit of her abdomen. How could something be so sweet, so satisfying, yet still make her want, make her need...what? She didn't know; she only knew that if she didn't get it, these flames would consume her.

Her hands slid from his neck to his shoulders, and the feel of that sleek skin beneath her fingers, stretched taut over hard muscle, sent another ripple of heat through her to add to the blaze. She couldn't stop the little moan of pleasure that escaped her.

Con heard it through the haze that was sapping his sanity and felt the fiery touch of her fingers on the skin of his back. He groaned, low and deep, and thrust his tongue deeper. God, she felt so good, tasted so good; she was all soft, smooth fire, and he had to have more even if it burned him. His hands slid down her back to the edge of the sweatshirt, then up under it. The hot, living silk of her skin did incredible things to his fingers, sensitizing them to the point of near pain, and he had to wait a moment before he could move.

Shiloh's gasp at the feel of his hands on her skin was lost in their kiss. She wanted them everywhere, those strong, supple hands, wanted them everywhere with an urgent need she'd never experienced and didn't try to understand. She'd given up trying to understand any of this; she could only feel, and she didn't care.

A little moan of protest rose from her when his lips left hers, but it changed to a gasp of pleasure when he pressed his mouth to her cheek, her jaw, then down the long lines of her neck. Her head lolled back, offering that slender column to him, while the rest of her body tried to seek the hot caress of his hands. The effort made her twist in his arms with an innocent sensuality that brought another groan from deep within him.

Con's hands slid up her slender back beneath the bulky shirt, then, irresistibly, around to where the full swell of her breasts began. Just that slight curve, that beginning of womanly flesh, ripped at him, made his body surge to raging fullness. Every muscle clenched, as if all of them were connected to that hot, aching tightness between his legs. He buried his face in the hollow of her neck, feeling the pulse pounding beneath his lips.

"Oh, yes..."

It was barely a whisper as Shiloh arched to him, at the same time letting her hands slip down the hard muscles of his back. She tightened her grasp urgently, pressing him closer even as she knew it wouldn't be enough. She wanted more, so much more, more than she had ever wanted. It didn't matter why it had to be him; all that mattered was that only he could rouse this need in her, and only he could ease it.

Con heard her breathy sigh, and heat shafted through him. She moved, the soft fullness of her breasts pressing against his chest. Even through the sweatshirt he could feel her nipples, twin points of searing heat. In that moment he would have given his life to feel them naked against his skin, and his hands went unstoppably to the hem of the shirt. He tugged at it almost angrily, wanting to be rid of the barrier. He wanted her naked with him; he wanted to see, to touch, to stroke. He wanted her beneath him, on top of him; he didn't care, as long as it was naked skin to naked skin.

When she realized what he was doing, Shiloh felt a split second of surprise that she wasn't trying to stop him. Then she nearly laughed; the calm, reasoning Shiloh who would have done that had gone up in flames at the first touch of his lips. She wriggled free of the offending sweatshirt.

"Oh, God."

She heard his low, huskily whispered words, saw his eyes on her breasts, and her nipples tingled, hardened. She should have felt shy, she thought, but instead she felt only pride that her body could bring that look to his eyes. Had she been able to speak, she would have begged him to do more than look; she wanted those hands that had left that trail of fire on her back to touch her warm, waiting flesh.

Even as she thought it, he moved. His hands came up slowly to almost reverently cup those firm curves. The blood that had been pulsing through him hotly at the sight of her nipples rising to his gaze, turned to molten lava at how they tightened to pebble hardness at the first touch of his hands to their lush fullness.

She was so beautiful, he thought numbly, unable to believe the feel of that soft yet firm flesh rounding into his palms, more than filling them with their abundance. And the way she had responded just to his look... He hadn't even touched those rosy crests and they were already hard and peaked. He heard an odd, choked sound and was only aware it had come from him when he realized he was shifting his hips, trying to ease that pulsing, pounding pressure.

He was afraid to let his fingers stray to those enticing, begging peaks. He was on the edge already, and it had been so long, the thought of embarrassing himself completely wasn't out of the realm of possibility. But then she moved, arching her back as if offering them to him, and he was lost.

A sharp little cry of surprised pleasure broke from her as his fingers caught and caressed her tingling nipples. Oh, God, she hadn't known it would feel like that, hadn't known it would send little rockets of flaming sensation to that growing pool of heat expanding inside her.

At the sound he buried his face in the valley between her breasts, but his fingers never stopped moving, flicking, tugging gently, until she cried out again, then again.

"Con. Oh, Con."

Con shuddered. He'd never heard his name spoken like that before, and it echoed sweetly in his ears. He lifted his head to look at her, to see the green eyes wide and hot with passion, to see her lips parted with her rapid breathing. Keeping his eyes on her face, he lowered his head to one breast, capturing the nipple between his lips and flicking it with his tongue.

What he saw in her face then, the pure, shocked pleasure, the flame that leapt in the green depths before the thick lashes lowered and her head fell back, sent an explosive burst of heat racing along nerves that were already strained to the breaking point.

He'd never realized, never known, that giving pleasure could bring so much pleasure. Just knowing that he could do this for her, that she was letting him, did more for him than any of the casual encounters he'd had in the past. If he died right now, which at the moment seemed entirely possible, he would die having felt more than he ever had before.

When his hot, wet mouth left her breast, Shiloh couldn't suppress her moan of disappointment. But again he turned it to pleasure as he nuzzled her other breast and his lips found the taut, puckered flesh that eagerly awaited him. She gasped as he suckled it, tugging it deep into his mouth, making her arch once more, thrusting her throbbing breasts up to him.

"Yes," he murmured against her skin, his hot breath feathering over her in a shivery caress.

His hand slid up to her other nipple, still wet and tingling from his mouth, and his fingers caught and rolled the erect tip with slow care. She was writhing now, her hips beginning to move in a rhythm as old as time. Shiloh thought she was going to fly apart as she moved involuntarily, desperately, striving for something she wasn't sure she could reach. She clutched at him, clinging to him as if he were the only solid thing left on this whirling flight.

"Please," she gasped without knowing what she was pleading for. She only knew that if she didn't get it, she was going to shatter into a million pieces.

That tiny whispered plea broke Con. He was about to explode, and if he didn't ease this hammering need right now, he truly would die. He kicked away the tangled covers, then tugged at the pale blue scrap of lace across her hips, the last barrier between them. He could feel the heat of her as he slid her panties down the trim curve of her hips, and when his fingers brushed the reddish brown curls and found them damp with her own need, he groaned harshly.

She did want him. His last shred of sanity vanished with the knowledge that she was hot and wet and ready, and he couldn't wait any longer. He had to have her, had to bury himself in that waiting heat. The part of his mind that would have wondered at this mindless creature he'd become, this new and strange being who was shamelessly admitting a need that was so much more powerful than himself, had been reduced to barely glowing coals by green-eyed fire.

It was the same part of his mind that would have noticed her slight awkwardness as he pressed her beneath him and slipped between her thighs. Would have noticed the touch of apprehension in her eyes at the feel of his hot, rigid manhood against that silken skin. He could feel the heat radiating from her, and it drew him inexorably forward until the tip of his hardened flesh was probing her velvet softness.

She was so ready, as ready as he was, and he could almost feel that slick, wet heat surrounding him already. He wanted to go slowly, to savor every moment of her body's acceptance of him, yet he wanted to bury himself in her with one fierce thrust that would take his breath away. But he didn't dare, for he knew he was much too close, and that the moment he was fully inside her it would be all he could do to hold back....

Something was wrong, and the fact was beginning to penetrate the thick haze of pleasure that clouded his mind the way a cool breeze cleared smoke. That breeze fanned the embers of the part of his mind that could still function, and a tiny flicker of reason returned.

He was meeting resistance. She was so slick and wet it should have been easy, he should already be deep inside her, he should . . .

Like a jagged bolt of lightning, the realization hit. He froze, every muscle taut and bulging, every vein standing out with the strain. As if some other part of him had been registering it all along, he saw in his mind the uncertainty with which she had moved to accept him, saw the apprehension that had shone faintly in her emerald eyes.

A harsh, ragged groan ripped from deep in his throat, and with a greater effort than any he had ever made in his life, he pulled back. His body screamed in protest, his throbbing shaft demanding her heat, his mouth crying out to be returned to her breast. He hung there a moment, suspended above her, trembling with the force of the conflict. At last, in agonizing slow motion, his mind won and he rolled away to collapse on his back in a shuddering, aching heap.

It wasn't going to stop. He was going to lie here for the rest of his life in this throbbing, hurting puddle. He groaned inwardly, wishing he had died. And thinking that if he could ever move again, he might just help that wish along a little.

He didn't know how long he'd lain there before the sound reached him. He'd shut his eyes and tried not to hear anything, but this sound was unavoidable. He made himself look.

She was huddled in the corner of the bunk, curled in on herself like a mortally wounded animal. And she was crying. Not wild, hysterical sobs, but a quiet flow of tears that was infinitely more disturbing. She'd been through hell, she'd been frightened, attacked, chased and shot at, and never once had she let it overcome her. Yet now she was crying.

"God, Shiloh, don't!" He pulled her trembling body into his arms. "It's all right. I...stopped in time. You're still...intact."

She was suddenly a wild thing in his arms, thrashing, pushing, kicking until she was free. She crouched on her knees before him, an odd combination of wildness and pained confusion flashing in her eyes.

"Is that what you think?" She dashed the tears from her cheeks in an abrupt, jerky gesture. "That I was crying because I...I thought I wasn't a virgin anymore?"

He looked at her blankly, confused. His body wasn't confused; the sight of her, her emotions robbing her of any awareness of her own nudity, her hair tousled from his hands and her bare breasts heaving with the quickness of her breathing, the nipples still taut and erect and glistening from his mouth, was almost too much for him.

"Do you think I cared about that? That I'm some stupid little girl who didn't know what she was doing?" She took a rapid, gasping breath, and despite her efforts her voice broke. "I was...crying because you...started again, and then...like on the beach..." She lowered her eyes as the tears began to slip silently down her flushed, damp cheeks once more. "I thought you...wanted me, but—"

A short, sharp sound came from him, making her look up. "But nothing," he said hoarsely, his voice tight with self-condemnation. "I wanted you so badly nothing else mattered. Not that you're Linc's baby sister, not that you could have gotten pregnant...and it damned near didn't matter that you're a virgin." He took a short, harsh breath. "Damn it, you should have told me. I would have stopped. I never would have started."

"It's not something you advertise. And I didn't care."

"Well I do!" He groaned under his breath. "Great," he muttered. "I nearly rape the sister of damn near the only friend I've got, never even think about protecting her—"

"It wasn't rape." Her voice had gotten stronger, steadier. "And besides, I couldn't have."

"What?"

"Gotten pregnant." He stared at her, bewildered. "It's a...hormonal imbalance, the doctor said. If I ever want to get pregnant, I'll have to take something."

That she was talking so matter-of-factly about what he had nearly done enraged him for some reason. "It doesn't make any difference. I didn't know that, and I almost—"

"And I'm not anybody's 'baby' sister. Linc is my brother, but I'm a grown woman, not a child. I make my own decisions."

"You—"

"And one of those decisions was not to have sex until it felt absolutely right."

"God, Shiloh, don't do this to me...."

She went on as if he hadn't spoken. "And this feels...right. For the first time in my life."

"It's not that simple, damn it. This is no good—"

"It felt pretty good to me."

He sat up sharply. "Don't make a joke out of this. Not this. You—" He had to stop for a moment, swallowing tightly. "You waited this long...for what? To throw it away in the wrong place, at the wrong time, and sure as hell with the wrong man? You deserve more. You deserve better than..."

He stopped, looking away, but his unspoken "better than me" echoed as if he'd said it.

"And you're the one who gets to decide? That I get what I 'deserve' and not what I want?" She saw him suck in a breath, saw his stomach muscles quiver as if she'd hit him. "That's not your decision, Con. It's mine." She lifted her chin, not even bothering to wipe at the traces of tears. "Your decision is simple. Do you want me or not?"

"Damn!" He rolled out of the bunk in a convulsive movement. He stood beside it, staring down at her, aware of his own body as he never had been before, and knowing she was watching him. "Do I look like a man who doesn't want you?"

He saw her eyes lower, could almost feel her gaze brush his swollen, engorged shaft. It was too much. He turned on his heel and strode out of the small cabin. He unlocked the hatch and grabbed the cabin roof, lifting himself up without even touching the steps in a fierce, angry motion. He hoped the cove would stay deserted, because he had no intention of catering to anyone's modesty right now. He stepped up on the gunwale and threw himself naked into the chilly ocean.

Sometime during the night, fog had rolled in. It lay thick and gray and damp all around, obscuring the sun even as it accented the slightest sounds. The gentle slosh of the water in the cove as the *Phoenix* rode the slight swell was louder, the creaking of the rigging louder still. More than ever they seemed in a fantasy place, only now it was a place that, for the moment, would not release them; Shiloh was not about to try leaving in this.

She had too much else to think about, anyway. She had stayed awake last night, after having crept back to her bunk in a mood teetering between thoughtfulness and hurt. She had tried to resurrect some of her analytical powers, but had found them useless in contemplating the mystery of Connor McQuade. All she had to go on were the instincts she hadn't even known she had until he came into her life.

Trying to ignore the clamoring of a confused body that didn't understand why it had been denied, she had sat curled up against the bulkhead, wrapped in a soft, heavy blanket. Her mind had heard what he'd said, that she was Linc's sister, that he'd thought she could get pregnant, that she was a virgin. But her instincts told her that the real reason ran much deeper, and she had gotten her clue in that last emotional exchange.

Quite simply, he didn't think he was good enough for her. The thought made her hurt for him, that he thought so little of himself, and at the same time made her feel a half-guilty sense of pleasure that he thought so much of her. But most of all it assuaged her spirit and the pride that had been sorely battered; he hadn't stopped because he didn't want her.

No, she could never believe that. A flush had spread through her body as she remembered him, standing beside the bunk, gloriously, magnificently naked, aroused and utterly male. Lord, she thought, feeling her ignorance as never before, did it really work? Could she really take that potent, throbbing flesh inside her, all of it? She supposed she must be able to, the human race was still here, but oh, it seemed impossible.

She had shuddered, pulling the blanket up closer around her, her body loath to surrender the last clinging remnants of the pleasure he'd brought to her. He wanted her, she was certain now of that, and she was equally certain that he wasn't going to do a thing about it. He was caught up in some tangle of male honor and cynical self-deprecation. He'd said it was the wrong place, the wrong time, the wrong man. Then why was it the first time, the only time, in her life that it had felt right?

She almost laughed at the irony of it. More than one relationship she'd been in had ended because she'd declined that last step, thinking there had to be more than just a quiet affection. And now that she'd found the man who had proved her right, it was going to be over before it began because *she* wanted to take that last step. It figures, she thought dryly. You spend your whole life building your control and then fall for the first man who blows it away.

Fall for? She sat up stiffly at her own thought. Had she? For this dark, mysterious man who lived in shadow, who moved in that same grim, dangerous world her brother did, that same world that had almost taken her beloved father from her? The same world that had made survival a facet of her childhood, disguised as the imaginative "black hats" game?

Her thoughts had been interrupted then by the sound of Con's return to the boat. She had relaxed a little; she'd been half-afraid he would try to spend the night on the beach, and despite the warmth of the days, the nights knew winter was approaching, and he wasn't that long over the virus that had felled him.

She had heard him come below, then go back up, then nothing. She tried to regain her train of thought, but by then the emotional strain of the night was beginning to take its toll, and the warmth of the blanket was beginning to sap her strength. The last thing she remembered before waking to the fog was reaching for her pillow.

And now she sat looking out a porthole at a world that was gray and blurred, as if it, too, felt the pressure of something unfinished. She shivered, rubbing her bare arms, realizing that she had left her clothes in Con's bunk. She leaned over and tugged up the nylon suitcase, reaching hurriedly for a thick, warm sweater and a pair of jeans.

Barefoot, she went forward, pausing to flip the heater on low, trying to keep everything dry as well as warm. She would check the batteries later, although she knew the big 12-volt storage units had more than enough to keep them going for three or four days without having to turn on the generator.

She moved quietly in the galley, choosing hot chocolate over coffee on this shrouded morning. Should be pea soup, she thought wryly, a little surprised that she was able to joke, even with herself.

A few minutes later, steaming mug in hand, she eased open the hatch Con had left unlatched and started up on deck. She stopped dead on the third step when she got her first look at the cockpit. There, curled awkwardly on a hard bench too short for his long body, was Con, asleep under one of the blankets from his bunk.

Why on earth had he slept up here? she wondered. Obviously that trip below and then back had been for the blanket, but why hadn't he just gone back to bed? Was the thought of staying below with her, even nearly a boat length apart, so impossible? Once more she battled the hurt that rose in her.

Slowly she went up the rest of the way. Slowly, and she thought silently, but his head came up, his long, lean body coiling instinctively. Then he saw her and the tension faded, and he started to smile at her.

As if she could read his mind, she saw the memories flood back, sweeping that half-formed smile away before them. He jerked his head away, staring at the blanket he was wrestling with as he sat up. He had put on the pair of jeans she'd washed with her shirt yesterday; she wondered if he had meant to complete his rejection of her by rejecting her brother's clothes and returning to his own.

He shivered slightly before he could control it. He hadn't put on a shirt, and he pulled the blanket up over his chilled, bare shoulders. Shiloh tried not to remember what those shoulders had felt like beneath her hands, or how that muscled expanse of chest had felt crushing her breasts. With a steadiness she was proud of, she wordlessly offered him the steaming cup of cocoa.

He stared at her for a moment, his eyes shuttered and unreadable. Then he took it, nodding silently, wrapping his hands around it, savoring the heat. Shiloh went to pour a second cup, and when she came back he was propped against the cabin, sipping at the warming liquid. She slid the hatch closed; the little heater should have things nicely warm soon. She sat on the bench opposite him, curling her long legs under her.

The silence stretched out uncomfortably, made thicker by the eerie grayness around them; there was nothing to distract them from the fact that neither of them had said a word, nothing to even pretend to be looking at. Finally Shiloh worked up her nerve. She cleared her throat.

"Con?"

"Mm." It was the barest grunt of acknowledgment that she'd spoken. Here it comes, he thought. The hurt, the anger, the recriminations. And he couldn't blame her one damned bit.

"What were you dreaming about?"

His head snapped up. "What?" Couldn't she just once do what he expected?

"Last night. When I...you were dreaming. A nightmare."

"I...was?"

"You were talking. Saying 'no,' over and over. That's why I woke you."

He stared at her. "You...woke me...for that?"

She stared back at him, puzzled. "Yes. What did you think I—" She broke off abruptly. He had looked away quickly, but she had seen him flush, had seen the look of guilty chagrin that had overwhelmed that shuttered look in his eyes.

"Oh, Lord," she murmured.

He'd thought she'd come to him expecting him to make love to her. No wonder he'd looked at her so oddly at first. And no wonder he'd been so surprised, even angry, to find she'd never been with a man before. He'd been expecting experience and found a virgin.

And he had run like hell from the responsibility of being her first. And it would be a responsibility to him; she knew now how much like her brother he truly was. Deep down, beneath all the ice and behind all the walls, despite his own low opinion of himself, there was an honest, honorable core that was as untouchable in him as it was in her brother, in her father. It was why, she supposed, she had fallen in love with him.

She nearly gasped out loud at her own thought. Some-where, sometime, during that long, restless night, some quiet little part of her brain had been working on the ques-tion she'd asked herself. And come up with the answer. Yes, she had fallen. Hard. Had lost control as she had sworn she never would, and it had happened so subtly, so quickly, she hadn't even realized it until it was too late. Much too late. She loved Connor McQuade, and there was no turning back from it.

She stared down into her own steaming mug, afraid to look at him for fear that her newly dawned knowledge would be clear on her face. She had no illusions about the problems she had just brought down on herself. Having him find out what she'd just realized would only add to her troubles. He felt guilty enough already, she thought, with-out piling that on him, too. Besides, she added with a note of silent disgust, he was so set on thinking of her as "Linc's baby sister" that he would probably just write it off as some childish infatuation.

Well, she'd been dealing with some harsh realities when other kids had been playing on swings. She'd never really been a child, and she wasn't going to start acting like one now. She wasn't going to wear her heart on her sleeve or play games with him; she had that much pride left, at least. She swallowed once, forcing down the lump that had tightened her throat; then her chin came up. She was a woman, not a child, and he was damned well going to find that out.

Con had been watching her from the corner of his eye. He saw a string of emotions he couldn't fathom cross her delicate features, then saw that defiant chin come up in a movement he had already come to know. She'd made up her mind about something, and he could only hope it wasn't to hate him for what he'd nearly done. And for what he'd assumed, when in truth she'd only meant to free him from whichever one of the chronic, recurrent nightmares had gripped him last night.

She got to her feet, and he braced himself, not even trying to guess at what she would do; he'd been wrong every time so far.

"It should be warm below by now."

"What?" Was that all he could ever say?

"I turned the heat on. It should be warm by now. Unless you like the fog?" She raised an eyebrow at him.

She was going to play it perfectly, he thought. Like nothing had ever happened. Letting him off the hook.

"Shiloh . . ."

She looked down at him with an air of calm patience. "All right. Let's say it and get it over with. I hate big emotional scenes. So you're sorry, I'm sorry, each for our own reasons."

"But—"

"But what? You want to feel guilty?"

"I don't want to—I *do*." His lips tightened. "I almost took something I had no right to."

"Who does have the right?"

He looked at her, puzzled by the odd, husky softness that had come into her voice.

"Who?" she repeated.

"The man . . . you'll fall in love with, someday."

A soft smile curved her lips, bewildering him. "You're absolutely right," she agreed, and turned to slide open the hatch. He stared after her, caught gaping when she tossed casually over her shoulder, "And 'almost' only counts in horseshoes."

He sat there, staring into the unrelenting grayness. His effort to figure out the meaning behind that enigmatic smile soon surrendered to the vivid image of Shiloh finding that man he'd spoken of, the man who would have the right to claim what she had nearly given him last night. That man would take that gift, and Con hoped to God he realized how priceless it was. He'd damned well better put a ring on her finger and give her the rest of his life, he thought furiously. She deserved nothing less.

A vision formed in his head of Shiloh naked beneath that faceless figure, entwining her long, lithe legs with his, her fingers stroking his back, wanting. As she had wanted him last night.

A strangled groan escaped him, and he shuddered. He wanted to kill that nameless, faceless man he'd created, wanted to strangle him with his own hands for touching her, for taking her.

Damn! He swore softly, bitterly, jerking himself to his feet in a sharp, angry movement. He was going crazy, he had to be, threatening characters he'd dreamed up himself. By the time she found that man, he would be long gone and would never know. Until, maybe, someday when Linc might casually mention that his little sister had married, or had had a baby...

Something wrenched and tore deep inside him at the thought. Shiloh round and glowing and pregnant with the child of that nameless, faceless man from the future. And Linc, the happily proud uncle of some no doubt brightly blond youngster with Shiloh's emerald eyes.

"Are you coming in, or shall we try to heat the whole island from here?"

He froze, not daring to look over to where she stood in the hatchway. He had the strangest feeling that what he'd been thinking about would be crystal clear to her.

"Yeah," he muttered, steeling his features to careful blandness before he turned and went down into the golden warmth.

Chapter 9

The fog burned off by early afternoon, but the weather channel told them it would be back soon. Shiloh had spent the rest of the morning puttering around, checking various items of gear she hadn't had time to check before their hasty departure and hadn't taken the time to yesterday.

Yesterday. It seemed weeks ago instead of merely hours. And the night when she'd come home to find him on her bed seemed years ago, not merely days. Five days. Was it possible to fall in love with someone in five days?

It must be, she thought as she recoiled and hung the mainsail halyard, because you've done it. You, Miss Cool, Calm and Collected. Wouldn't Mandy love to see you now? She'd always said there would come a day...

Con was trying his hand at fishing off the stern with the one rod Wayne kept aboard. They had reached a tentative peace, mainly due to Shiloh's refusal to act as if anything were wrong. Her determination faltered only once, when she found her clothes folded neatly on her bunk. With a sudden flash of insight, she knew that finding the clothes he had torn from her still in his bed was what had driven him abovedecks last night. But she recovered quickly and said nothing when she went back on deck.

He had been wary at first, the memories of last night seared into his brain, but she ignored the undercurrent and returned to the lighthearted banter they'd indulged in before. Finally he accepted it, knowing he had little choice, yet unable to shake the cloud he sensed hovering between them. He had never liked loose ends; they had a way of snapping back and knocking you out when you least expected it.

He cringed at his own words; thinking about her as a loose end made his stomach churn. He was trying to put her in one of the slots he made for people while he was working: helpful, nonhelpful, enemy, unknown, loose end. And friend. He'd had to add that one after Linc had come along. But no matter how he tried, Shiloh Reese just wouldn't slip neatly into any slot. Unless he invented a new one just for her.

Unpredictable, maybe. She was certainly that. And stubborn. He stared down into the water, thinking over the last five—God, was it only five?—days. So add brave to the list. And gutsy and smart and quick, and strong and tough . . . and soft and warm and beautiful—and sexy. Oh, yeah, McQuade, don't forget that. As if his body would let him.

He rather gruffly declined her offer to join her in a swim when the sun finally broke through. He didn't trust himself within ten yards of her in that damned scrap of a bathing suit. But it didn't stop him from watching her, from admiring her smooth, effortless stroke, or keeping his eyes glued to the slim, graceful figure that strolled along the narrow strip of beach.

He saw her approach a large patch of brush, then jump back, startled. He dropped the fishing rod, careless of where it landed, and stood up. He relaxed when she laughed, then wondered how on earth he could tell from here. Had he been studying her so closely that he knew from the tilt of her head, the set of her slender shoulders, that she was laughing?

He hadn't been aware of it, not in the way he knew he studied the people who were the suspects in his work, or the ones he might have to use. Yet he seemed to know her every expression better than he'd ever known anyone. Now if he could only figure out how that agile brain of hers worked...

Much to his own amazement, shortly after she returned from her swim, he caught a fish. Not being much of an ocean fisherman, he had no idea what it was, but it was a foot-and-a-half long, and, Shiloh assured him, quite edible.

"I know all the poisonous ones," she told him, laughing at his expression. Then she relented. "It looks like a yellowtail. Not quite tuna fish, but close."

"Oh." He looked relieved, And about twelve years old when he looked at her and said, "Can we have it for dinner?"

She laughed again, but she was blinking rapidly against the sudden stinging of her eyes. It was as if she'd gotten a brief, fleeting glimpse of a different Con, younger, happier, with a touching vulnerability in the place of his icy shell. She wondered if he'd ever been like that for more than brief, fleeting moments.

"Only if you clean it," she said when she could speak again. "And guillotine it. I could never eat anything that was looking back at me."

He laughed, that shining moment lasting just a little longer. "Aye, aye, cap'n. Find me a knife and I'll behead this beast."

That night she cooked the fish in a sauce of what was left of the wine, butter and whatever herbs she could find that sounded good. Served over the last of the rice, it was delicious, and they finished it to the last scrap.

The fog had rolled in right on schedule. It made them feel even more secure; if they couldn't see anything, then neither could they be seen. By anything or anyone. Shiloh made a brief call to her father, who reported all was well.

"Wish that ungrateful son of mine would at least call his old man once in a while," he whined in a perfect imitation of a crotchety old man. Con could tell it was an imitation by the grin on Shiloh's face.

"Well, we didn't really expect to hear from him. He'll be in touch when he can. We're on a time-out for the moment anyway, so don't worry."

"Don't tell me not to worry, girl. You sure this friend of yours knows the rules of this game?"

Shiloh studied the radio intently. "Oh, yes. I'm perfectly safe, even if he does have this habit of making up some rules of his own as he goes along."

Con flushed, but she gave no indication that her words had had a double meaning.

"Sometimes you have to," her father said. "When does play resume?"

"Tomorrow night, maybe. Thursday at the latest."

"I'll be ready. Take care, baby."

Shiloh held the microphone for a moment or two, as if loath to sever the connection. At last, very slowly, she hung it up.

"I'm worried about him," she said softly. "He's all alone there, and he doesn't move very quickly anymore...."

Con lowered his eyes, feeling sick. He'd gotten her into this, and therefore her father, too, and there wasn't a thing he could say to change it. So he said nothing. In her worry, Shiloh took his silence for indifference and whirled on him.

"Wouldn't you be worried if it was your father?"

He laughed, short, harsh and bitter. "I doubt it."

She stared at him, taken aback. He was sitting at the navigation station, toying with a pencil, his eyes fixed on it in the way of someone who wasn't seeing the object at all.

"You really mean that," she murmured in wonder.

When he spoke, his voice had the same bitter undertone as that mirthless chuckle, and the same hesitant, broken cadence she'd noticed before whenever he spoke of something personal. His fingers tightened around the pencil.

"My father...walked out on my mother before I was born. He didn't want her anymore...and he never wanted me." His thumbnail was digging gouges into the soft wood of the pencil. "She was only sixteen...."

Shiloh held her breath, afraid that any slight sound would stop the broken flow of words.

"She...couldn't get a job.... She'd quit school to...run away with him. After I was born...she did the only thing she could. She was broke.... Her parents said they'd take her back if...if she got rid of me. But she wouldn't."

His eyes had gone flat, unfocused, and Shiloh knew he was deep into the painful memories. When he went on, his voice was low and strained.

"She used to leave me with the lady downstairs. I didn't know...until later. I thought all mothers...went out every night, all dressed up." He took a deep, shuddering breath. "When I was five, one of her...customers beat her to death."

The pencil snapped, the sound echoing like a gunshot and making Shiloh jump. A jagged splinter of wood dug into his palm, and blood welled up immediately. He never even blinked.

And then Shiloh was there, kneeling beside him, taking his bleeding hand in hers. His head came up in a sharp, jerky motion, and his eyes fastened on her face. He saw, for the second time, tears brimming in her eyes. The faraway, unfocused look vanished.

"Don't," he said harshly, hating the thought of her pity. He lifted his other hand to her cheek. "Not for me."

"Not just for you," she whispered. "Your mother...she must have loved you so much...."

He stared at her. "You...you're crying...for my mother?"

No one had ever expressed anything but disgust for his mother; no one had ever believed she had truly loved her son, that her life had not been her choice.

The first of the crystalline tears slid over the silken skin of her cheeks. "What a horrible thing to have to do," she said raggedly. "And what a beautiful thing to love your child enough to do it."

Con paled. "I...they never...she was always 'that woman.' That I was better off without her. A prostitute for

a mother. They thought she'd always been...that I
was...from one of her johns. I tried to tell them...."

"But who listens to a child?" The tears were falling rapidly now, and Shiloh made no effort to wipe them away; her
hands were holding his too tightly. She could feel the little
tremors that were going through him, could guess what this
was costing this very strong, very private man.

"She was...always waiting...hoping he'd come back....
She used to tell me about him...." He gulped in a breath.
"He walked out on a pregnant sixteen-year-old girl, and she
never once said a word against him...."

He shuddered, and she could sense him trying to pull together the remnants of his control. She sensed, as she had
been able to all those years ago when her brother had come
home from the war, that he had gone as far as he could go
right now, that any more would make him shut down completely, possibly forever. She drew on her own control and
this time found it there, for him.

"I'll get the first-aid kit. That needs cleaning out."

She went for the box, taking her time to give him a moment to pull himself together. When she came back, he was
studying his bloody hand, and the tremors had stopped. He
bore her ministrations quietly, stoically, silently, until she
went to put an adhesive bandage on the small wound.

"Leave it. It's fine."

She hesitated, then nodded and put everything away and
went to put the kit back under the step. Her mind was reeling. She knew in that instinctive part of her that had only
come to life since she'd met him that he'd never told anyone, not even Linc, what he'd told her tonight. Every word
had held the raw pain of being ripped from somewhere deep
inside him where it had hidden, had festered, for years.

It made what else she knew of him, that he had gone on
to college, to law school, with no help other than the scholarship he had earned, even more incredible. A sense of regret filled her that the woman—the girl, really—who had
sacrificed her pride and eventually her life for her child
couldn't know what he had done. With a feminine, mater-

nal knowledge she'd never experienced before, she knew
with certainty just how proud that girl would have been.

When she came back he was sitting at the main table. He
looked from his hand to her still damp cheek, where the cut
from the shattered windshield had nearly healed in the fresh
air and saltwater.

"Remind me to buy Wayne a new first-aid kit. We've
made a dent in this one."

It wasn't what he wanted to say. He wanted to tell her how
much her tears had meant, tears for a woman who'd had no
one to cry for her except a bewildered little boy. He wanted
to tell her what a relief it had been to talk about it, even
while he was stunned at the fact that he had. He wanted to
tell her things he'd never told anyone in his life, wanted to
forget the harsh training of a lifetime and pour out his soul
to her. Only the inviolate set of rules that had been ham-
mered into him in the hardest of ways stopped him.

For a long time they sat in silence, the only sounds the
oddly emphasized clanging of the rigging on the mast and
the gentle slapping of water against the hull. Shiloh sipped
at the hot chocolate she'd made again, trying not to be too
obvious about watching him. He was deep in thought, running one finger idly around the rim of his own cup in a way
that sent odd little shivers down her spine.

At last he let out a sigh of disgust and seemed to come
back to the present. He saw her looking at him, and his
mouth twisted wryly.

"I'm getting real tired of feeling so stupid," he muttered. "No matter how many times I go over it, or how
many ways I twist it, there's still one thing I can't figure
out."

Join the club, Shiloh thought, but she knew he wasn't
speaking personally; he was back at WestAir. "What?"

"Why they waited so long. Why they took a chance of my
finding something out before they came after me. If the
joker is that high up, they had to have known from day
one."

"Maybe they thought they had it so well hidden you
wouldn't find anything."

"Then why come after me at all? Why not let me prowl around, come up empty and give them a clean bill of health?" He shook his head wearily. "It couldn't have taken him two weeks to figure out he had to get rid of me."

"He?"

"Fred Wilkens. He's the head of Research and Development at WestAir." He stopped, looking a little surprised. When had he surrendered all reservations about involving her further? Somehow, after entrusting her with a large part of his soul, trusting her with his work seemed simple.

"And Moose and Company's boss?"

He nodded, in his eyes a salute to her quick grasp of the situation. "Since the chances were good that the leak was in R and D, I started with him."

"And struck oil."

"Apparently. But why did he wait? For all he knew I could already have been poking around in his files. I know now he's the top dog at WestAir in this sellout. It's not like he had to wait for somebody else's decision. Once he knew I was in, that should have been it. I should have been history right then." He ran a hand through the thick darkness of his hair, obviously frustrated.

"What if...he didn't know right away? About you, I mean."

Con shook his head slowly. "With the connection he's got? He had to know as soon as the joker did. Just like he knew what other companies had the resources to complete the work WestAir had started. And how to get them the plans. He's gotten away with it for a long time, and not by being afraid to do what's necessary. And fast."

He grimaced. "Hell, they killed an FBI agent. What's one company man after that? It doesn't make sense that he let me poke around for two weeks before he did anything."

"Maybe he doesn't know how good you are."

The instant spurt of pleasure he felt at her words faded as his own judgment stepped in. "Yeah," he muttered. "So good I'm out before I even start."

"So good that without even starting, you know where the leak is and who the seller is."

He stared at her; he hadn't thought of it that way at all. He couldn't quite smother the smile that tugged at his lips at her spirited defense of him. Loyalty, it seemed, went along with the bestowal of faith. He felt like he'd been given a prize he wasn't at all sure he deserved.

"Those are the most important things, aren't they?"

He tried to concentrate on her question instead of the kernel of warmth her words had kindled in some cold, long-forgotten place deep inside him.

"That depends," he said, running a hand through his tousled hair, "on who the joker is."

Shiloh considered that for a moment. "Who could he be? I mean, who has that kind of access?"

"Joe does, but he's gone for a month."

"Who else?"

"Me." He gave her a sideways look. "I didn't do it."

She wrinkled her nose at him. "I just didn't real-ize . . . does everyone on the troubleshooting team have that kind of clearance?"

"No."

"Then it has to be somebody who's getting access with-out the clearance then, doesn't it?"

He studied his now empty mug. "Aren't you even going to mention Sam?"

"No."

"Why?"

"Because it's not him."

He looked up at her then. "Just because I said so?"

She nodded. "We have to trust him as much as he trusts you. That isn't exactly a standard security clearance you have there." She added softly. "You have to trust some-body."

I trust you. The words formed instantly in his head, so quickly he was afraid for a moment that he'd spoken them. But would it matter if he did? He did trust her. He had to admit it now. She had given her trust to him with very little reason. And she had given it to Sam with even less reason. How could he deny her what she deserved in return?

Yes, he trusted her, as much as he trusted her brother, even as he was aware of what he was risking, even as all those years of bitter experience told him he was a fool. Well, he thought glumly, it wouldn't be the first time. But it might well be the last. He wasn't sure he cared anymore. If he turned out to be wrong about Sam or her or Linc, he wasn't sure he would care about anything. Ever.

He needed this swim, Con thought as they made their way to the small beach once more. It had been a hellish night, filled with dreams that made the one he'd had in the loft seem innocent by comparison. More than once he'd awakened in a sweat, clenched fists wadding his blanket into knots, and only the vivid memory of that moment's innocent apprehension in a pair of emerald eyes had kept him from going to her.

The fog had disappeared as quietly as it had arrived, leaving them with a sky that was searingly clear and blue, even at this early hour. The last day, he thought as he began to follow her up onto the sand. Sam would be back tomorrow. The waiting would be over. The inaction would be over. His time with Shiloh would be over.

It was for the best, his mind told him as he watched her walk up the slight slope ahead of him, her slender hips moving in that unconsciously sensuous way that sent wildfire racing along his nerves. He would walk away and never see her again, his mind insisted as he tried to tear his eyes away from the taut curves that so temptingly filled the green suit, tried not to think of how much he wanted to cup that trimly rounded flesh in his hands as he pulled her against him.

"Damn," he muttered.

He stopped dead, still waist deep in the water, knowing he didn't dare leave its protective coverage until he had himself under control. This is ridiculous, he told his rebellious body. He'd never been like this, even as a teenager, with hormones running amok.

But you've never known anyone like Shiloh Reese, either. That little voice was back, just as irritating as before.

Right, he growled silently. More importantly, she's never known a man like me. Or any other man, for that matter, not the way I want to know her. So just get yourself away from her, McQuade. She deserves a hell of a lot better than a bastard like you for a lover. Her first lover.

Lover. He looked up at the slender figure in the soft green swimsuit, stunned by the rush of chaotic thoughts that raced through his mind at the word. Not just a casual fling, a mutual expression of physical need, as all the past brief encounters of his life had been. Lover. And all the things the word implied. A relationship. A commitment. Love. All the things she would give—and would expect in return. And deserve. All the things he'd never given anyone, would never be able to give anyone.

He'd never cared before. He'd just accepted the fact that caring was not for him and never would be. He'd never missed it, convinced himself he never wanted it. Life was so much easier, so much simpler, when it was free of entanglements. Entanglements interfered with your work, gave your enemies levers to use against you, messed up your mind and could get you killed. He knew all that.

So why did the thought of walking out of her life fill him with an emptiness that made what he'd lived with all his life seem minuscule? For the first time in his life, the years that stretched ahead seemed colder, more vacant, than those he'd left behind.

"Are you all right?"

She had turned to look at him, a quizzical expression on her face.

"Fine." Considering that if I move out of this water you won't have to be a mind reader to know what I've been thinking. "I'll be there in a second."

Sure. And it'll probably snow here tomorrow. Gritting his teeth, he stared down at the water, willing himself to regain control. Swimming back to the mainland would have been easier, he thought grimly when, at last, he was relaxed enough to leave the chilly water. So much for the vaunted effects of cold water.

She was walking toward the brush that began to thicken at the mouth of the small canyon that had made the little cove. As he caught up with her, she glanced over her shoulder at him, a smile curving her soft mouth.

"I was looking for—"

Her words were cut off with a sudden gasp of shock as Con leapt, tackling her around the waist and throwing her to the ground. He came down on top of her, hunching over her, moving as if he were shielding her body with his own.

Shiloh didn't have the breath to speak, let alone scream. In the moment when she tried to take in enough air to do one or the other, she became aware of the odd posture of his body, the rigid tension of his every muscle. Then she heard the sound.

It was the slightest rustle in the brush, the merest whisper of branches moving. Followed by the parting of the leaves by a small head, mottled gray and white, with a pair of tiny horns and bright, curious eyes.

"That," Shiloh managed to say despite the difficulty of breathing with his full weight on her, "is what I was looking for."

Feeling more than a little silly, Con looked over his shoulder at the small goat that seemed mesmerized by their presence. She'd mentioned that a large herd of them lived on the island, he remembered now. And he remembered that moment when he'd watched her from the boat, when she'd come up to these same bushes and jumped back, startled. The tension drained from him, and he couldn't quite meet her eyes.

"I seem to spend a lot of time getting knocked off my feet with you around." In more ways than one, Shiloh added silently.

His eyes snapped up to hers then, the barest hint of color rising in his face. "I didn't . . . I thought it was . . ."

She knew what he meant. He hadn't thought at all. It had been pure instinct. He'd reacted instantly, fiercely and, to her amazement, protectively. The impression she'd gotten that he was protecting her body with his own had not been wrong. Pure instinct, she repeated to herself. Don't read any more into it than that.

"Quite a set of reflexes you have there, Mr. McQuade."

She seemed to have lost what breath she had regained; her words came out huskily, on a little rush of air. The sound of them sent a shiver down his spine.

She was looking up at him, those green eyes alight with something he couldn't name. The effects of that sudden spurt of adrenaline faded, leaving him all too aware of the sudden harshness of his own breathing and the way his heart had slowed from reaction-induced racing to a heavy, pulsing beat that echoed in his ears.

The tension drained from his muscles, leaving them slack and useless, and he sagged atop her. He tried to push himself away, but nothing seemed to be working; his body would listen to nothing, was aware of nothing except how she felt beneath him. He could feel the endless silk of her legs against his, the quickened thud of her heart.

Shiloh couldn't seem to breathe, and it didn't seem to matter. Her entire being was concentrated on the pair of bottomless blue eyes that stared down at her. And on what she could read in them: the awareness of her, the need, the growing heat, the determination, the anger. She wondered if the anger was at her or at himself. The question had barely formed in her mind when the heat swirled up in those blue depths, overcoming all else, and his mouth came down on hers with the sudden fierceness of an attacking hawk.

She meant to protest. She couldn't go through this again, couldn't take another rejection. But at the first touch of his firm, warm lips, she was lost. As if he were breathing fire into her, she melted beneath his touch, her arms going without question to circle his neck, her lips parting eagerly for his questing tongue.

The small sliver of her mind that was still functioning rang out a warning, a tiny red flag of danger that said she was surrendering the control she'd spent her life building, and to a man who would probably reject her again. She saw it, heard it, and couldn't make herself care. Couldn't make herself care about anything except the blaze he was kindling.

His tongue was tracing her lips, tasting, teasing; it wasn't enough. Tentatively she reached out with her own tongue, the tip brushing his. It was the barest of touches, a quick, split second of contact; it was the match to the tinder. She felt his groan in the vibration deep in his chest before she heard the smothered sound of it against her mouth.

He invaded her mouth then, plunging, demanding, sending ripples of sensation through her. Her hands clutched at him, slender fingers tangling in the thick, wet hair as she clung to him. Her tongue met his now, all hesitancy forgotten, dancing, twisting, tasting, needing. Her fingers tightened, pressing him closer, wanting, needing, more.

A little sound of protest rose from her as his tongue withdrew. Without thought her own followed, seeking, then stopping as she reached the boundary of his lips. His mouth went suddenly soft, coaxing, and she responded with a tentative swipe of her tongue over his lips.

Shiloh was stunned by the shudder that went through him at that tiny touch, and more stunned by the echoing ripple that raced along her own nerves. She probed forward, the tip of her tongue sliding into the hot depths of his mouth, flicking over the even ridge of his teeth.

He groaned again, low and deep and harsh. His hands cupped her face, tilting her head back to intensify the kiss, his tongue urging hers on until she was deep in that wet, luring heat. He shifted atop her, and she was suddenly aware of the hot, urgent hardness of him through the two thin, damp layers of cloth. The feel of him, rigid and ready, pressing against her belly, sent explosive little bursts of flame up from that place inside her, sent them spiraling upward to meet and collide with the conflagration he had begun with his mouth. A low moan, the only sound she could make to express this need she'd never felt before, broke from deep within her.

And then he was gone. He was gone, and she lay there shivering in the cold left by the sudden removal of his searing heat. Shaking, she opened her eyes. He was sitting a careful six inches away, staring at her with a pained longing that was frightening in its intensity. She stared back, her body still throbbing with need and utterly confused. And hurt.

"Wha—" She swallowed tightly and tried again, her voice a harsh, pained whisper. "What do you want from me?"

His eyes closed, and the expression on his rugged face was nothing short of agonized. "Shouldn't that be what do *you* want from *me?*" His tone matched his look. "But I already know. And I can't give it to you." The thick, dark lashes lifted; his eyes were as tortured as his face. "I can't, Shiloh."

Shiloh sat up, conscious of dragging air in through parted lips, of the aching heaviness of her breasts, the tingling tightness of her nipples, and most of all a new, strange hollowness deep and low inside her.

"I didn't…ask you for anything." Her voice shook, and a small spurt of anger at her own weakness stabbed through her.

Con let out a small, pained burst of air. "You don't have to ask. It's what you are, who you are. You want—deserve—things I can't give you."

The tiny flicker of anger sparked, then caught inside her. Only now it was directed at him and his infuriating tendency to insist on making her decisions for her.

"We've had this discussion before, as I recall. Who appointed you to decide what I deserve? And," she added, drawing her knees up under her so she could meet his eyes, "where do you get off telling me what I want?"

He winced, but she couldn't seem to get a rein on her rising temper. She was full of so many roiling emotions that she couldn't begin to sort them out and knew only that she was angry at his dictatorial manner and hurt that, when for the first time in her life she knew what it was to want a man, he wouldn't take what she offered.

It stung more than just her pride; it brought painfully to the fore the doubts that had arisen recently, the fear that the price she had paid for her considerable control had been her femininity. She drew a deep breath.

"Let me get this straight. I'm a stupid little child who's playing with fire, and you're the big, bad spy, who also happens to have the right to make all my decisions for me, since I must be incapable of doing it myself. I never realized you had to have sex before you could think—"

"Shiloh, stop it." Con's voice was dull, weary.

"I'll stop. As soon as I find out what it is I want. Since you seem to be the only one who knows, why don't you tell me?"

He turned his head away, closing his eyes as her words bit deep. She saw a shudder go through him and suddenly felt as if she'd kicked a wounded man, a man who was down and hurt. Her anger drained away, and when she spoke again, the edge had gone from her voice.

"What, Con? What is it you think I want?"

For a long moment she thought he wouldn't answer, but she'd learned to wait, had come to know how difficult it was for this lone wolf to open up. When the words came, they were harsh and strained.

"You...need someone who can be there for you. Who can promise you a future. Hell, I can't even promise tomorrow."

Shiloh stared at him, wondering if he even realized what he'd admitted about his feelings for her.

"I didn't ask for tomorrow," she said slowly.

"You don't have to ask," he answered. "It's just who you are. You're not the kind for... casual relationships. If you were, you wouldn't still be..."

"A virgin? We're back to that again?" Her eyes were snapping, her anger returning full force. "What do you want me to do, apologize? Say I'm sorry I haven't been to bed with every guy that came along?"

"Damn it, Shiloh..."

"Nice double standard you use, McQuade." She cut him off acidly. "Tell you what, I'll just go find someone without your scruples, one of those macho guys who gets a kick out of...deflowering maidens, isn't that what they call it?"

"Shut up!" Con snapped. The idea of her going to someone else, making love with someone else, was so painful that the heavy ache in his groin was momentarily overwhelmed by the instant rebellion of his mind and body at the thought.

"Why? Just because you don't want me doesn't mean somebody else won't." She took in a gulp of air, ashamed of herself, of the way she was acting, but unable to stop herself. "Somebody who isn't all bogged down in what they think I want..." Her words faded as she stared at him, huddled there on the sand, muscles tensing as if each word was a blow. "Do you think I'll lay some kind of claim on you? Is that it? That I'll expect you to...to make an honest woman of me or something?"

He looked at her then. "You should," he said tightly.

Her eyes widened. "You think I'd expect you to marry me? You think that's what I want?"

"Not me. I'm not stupid enough to think you'd—" He stopped and let out a long breath. "I mean, you...you've waited this long, you should wait for the man you will marry." *And I hate him, whoever he is.*

"Make up your mind," she said. "Is it the man I love, or the man I marry?"

He gaped at her, confused. "I...you wouldn't marry somebody you didn't love."

"What makes you think I ever plan on marrying anyone?"

"You will." His voice went suddenly flat. "You aren't made for anything less." *Remember that, McQuade. She isn't the kind for what little you can offer.*

"Oh, really." Shiloh was furious at his arbitrary assessment. This had somehow become about much more than her hurt feelings and frustrations. "Well, let me tell you, if my parents are any example, I'll pass."

Con's brows furrowed. "I thought your parents—"

"You don't know a damned thing about it," she snapped. "You didn't grow up watching a weeping, hysterical woman turn my father old before his time. You didn't see her whine constantly when he was hurt, not about him, but about herself. And then go out and flirt with every man in sight, saying that it was all right because her husband was a cripple.''

Con cringed, his stomach knotting in protest at the picture she was painting. ''I didn't know. You never mentioned her, so I guess I assumed . . . she was dead.''

''You assume one hell of a lot, McQuade.''

She was glaring at him, that angry light still leaping in her eyes, her slender body tense with it, her breasts rising and falling with her rapid breathing. She was all crackling energy, all fiery wrath, and she'd never been more beautiful to him. He knew instinctively that she would be the same in his arms, all fire and life, and the need to have her there was suddenly fierce and overwhelming. He wanted to plunge into that living flame, bury himself in her bright heat, let it sear away all the wasted, empty years. . . .

In the very act of reaching for her, he stopped. He stayed there, outwardly frozen, fighting an inner battle that was becoming harder and harder to win. Then he scrambled to his feet, backing away from her, toward the water, knowing it was his only chance of winning, of keeping himself from grabbing her, from taking her right there and then. For the first time in his life, Connor McQuade turned and ran.

Chapter 10

He knew she was behind him before he'd swum ten yards. Even with his head start she made it a race, her quick, even strokes pulling her close despite his longer, stronger ones. He pulled himself up over the rail of the boat, then sat watching her close the gap.

She swam, he thought, as she did everything else, giving it her best and fullest effort. She was strong and brave and bright, and unlike any woman he'd ever known. He watched as she reached the boat and pulled herself up into the cockpit.

She flipped her wet hair back out of her face with a toss of her head and stood looking at him. Never had the finely spun steel core of her been so evident, unexpectedly emphasizing the soft loveliness of her exterior. His eyes went over her helplessly, hungrily, loving her strength as much as her beauty.

"I wasn't through," she said tensely.

"I never thought you were." His voice was soft with a note she didn't recognize.

"Oh," she said sourly, "so you just decided to avoid the rest of the conversation."

"I should have known you wouldn't let me."

"So now I'm being stubborn?" She knew she sounded bitchy, but her emotions were still raw, and she couldn't help striking back.

"No. I was." He could imagine how she'd felt, to have waited so long only to be, in her eyes, rejected when she'd offered the most precious gift of herself. She was hurt, and he couldn't blame her. "I just . . ."

He stopped, his eyes going over her, up and down the trimly curved body in the skimpy green suit. His gaze lingered on the gentle swell of her hips and the full curve of her breasts, the tightness that had never gone away surging to aching fullness once again.

At last he met her eyes. They were so full of confusion, anger and pain that he had to look away again. When he could go on, his voice was low and husky.

"I was right, you know. It's the wrong place, the wrong time, and . . . I'm not the right man for you."

"So you've told me."

Shiloh sat down on a bench, despair sweeping over her. When she'd realized that she loved him, she had also acknowledged to herself that he didn't love her back. She hadn't expected him to, had known he had no room for love in his life. If she had entertained any idea that he would make room for her, she had discarded it with the cold rationality her familiarity with his world had instilled in her.

She would have been content, she thought, with just the fact that he wanted her. And she knew that he did; he'd left her no doubts. The hunger in his face was as obvious as the arousal of his body. But he didn't want her enough. Not enough to overcome his misguided reservations.

The irony of it bit deep. All these years of fighting off men who made her feel nothing but a mild curiosity, and now the one man in the world who could send her up in flames with a look wouldn't touch her.

Well, she'd be damned if she would beg. Her chin came up.

"Fine. You just hang on to that image you have of me as some wide-eyed little innocent who doesn't know anything.'' She looked at him balefully. "I may be inexperienced, but I'm not as naive as you think.''

The snap was back in her voice, the fire in her eyes. God, he thought, she never quit. She had more nerve, more backbone, than most of the men he'd ever worked with, more than most people he'd ever known.

He had to give it one last try, he thought, but his heart wasn't in it. "It's the circumstances, Shiloh. We're on the run together, we've been scared together. I've seen it before.''

"I'm sure you have. But don't insult me any further by telling me I haven't thought of that.''

Her hands were locked together in her lap, but her back was straight, her head high. Atta girl, Green-eyes, he applauded her silently, more than a little bemused by his own thoughts. She was sitting there giving him hell, and he was cheering her on.

Shiloh saw that look in his eyes, that glimmer of beguiled wonder. A new determination rose in her. She wouldn't beg, but she wouldn't give up without a fight, either. She wouldn't make it any easier for him by hiding the whole truth. She took a long breath before she went on steadily.

"Maybe I've never actually been there before, but I was raised knowing all about it. Linc told me enough about the...bonds that can be formed under stress. But it doesn't matter. Not here. Not now.''

She was looking at him so intently and with such a sudden rush of color in her cheeks that he couldn't stop himself from asking, "Why?''

Her color deepened, but she answered him levelly, holding his gaze with a strained effort that was visible in her eyes. "Because . . . you turned me to jelly long before I knew who—or what—you were.''

Con paled. "I . . . what?''

"I think that's really why I didn't call the police when I first found you. I just didn't want to admit it.''

He stared at her. He saw in her face that she knew what she was doing, what she was risking, laying her soul bare to him like that. And he knew as well that it had taken more courage than facing Moose and his partner, or that gang in the loft; he didn't know if he had that much courage himself. And she just sat there waiting, knowing he could destroy her so easily. And he knew it, too; knew that if he rejected her yet again, she would carry the scar forever.

No, he didn't know if he could match that courage, but he had to try. "I meant all those things," he said tightly, "but that wasn't all."

Something in his tone made her lift her eyes to his. "It wasn't?"

"No." He made himself meet her green-eyed gaze. "I just couldn't believe that you really meant it." He had the grace to admit what she'd said. "I did think you were naive. That you just didn't know what was happening."

"I knew *what* was happening," she said quietly. "I just didn't know that it could. To me, I mean."

How could she find the words? How could she explain the feeling of awe, her surprise that the body she thought she knew so well was still capable of shocking her after twenty-four years? "I've never felt that way, not with anyone."

Con felt his stomach knot at the same time that he felt his body heat with pleasure at her words. Desperately, he clung to his last doubt.

"You will someday. Wait, Shiloh. You don't—you can't really want me."

"Why?" She turned his question back on him, her eyes holding his relentlessly. "Why are you so certain of that?"

"I can't give you anything, can't promise you anything." His eyes swept over her. "God, Shiloh, look at yourself! You could have anybody."

She colored at his words but never released his gaze. "Have you looked in a mirror lately yourself?"

He flushed, that hot burst of pleasure flooding him again. He couldn't deal with this, he thought. He was out control; she was doing things to him he didn't understand. She was making him feel things he'd never felt, and she was doing it with words alone; God help him if she ever really touched him.

"You said I've waited a long time," she said softly. "And I have. Because no one ever made me feel the way it was supposed to feel. And now you're asking me to take the chance that somewhere, sometime, I just might find some-one else who... does this to me?"

He groaned, his body clenching so fiercely that it was all he could do to keep from curling up against the ache of it. He had given up trying to hide what she was doing to him; in the clinging nylon of the damp running shorts it was im-possible.

Shiloh saw in his face the fierceness of the battle raging inside him. And quite suddenly nothing mattered to her ex-cept easing the pain, stopping the damage he was inflicting on himself.

"Stop, Con." Her voice was a husky, gentle whisper that did nothing to ease his condition. "It's all right. Forget it. I understand. I'm sorry."

His eyes closed. Somehow that quiet, loving whisper was the last straw. He couldn't fight it anymore. It was over. "Shiloh..." It was a mere breath of sound.

"Quit tearing yourself apart. I had no right to put you in this position. I apologize for... throwing myself at you."

His blue eyes snapped open then. "As I recall," he said hoarsely, "I'm the one who keeps throwing you."

She just looked at him for a moment, aware of the new note in his voice. And of the heat of his gaze. It took her a moment to recognize the difference, that now, suddenly, nothing was at war with that heat, that there was no sign of his battle to fight it down.

When she realized what that meant, her breath left her in a rush and a small, tight kernel of matching warmth began to expand in that deep, low place inside her she hadn't known existed before him.

Con read the understanding in her eyes and saw her soft lips part on that explosive little breath. When she dropped her gaze, he slipped off the rail and stood before her.

"Look at me, Shiloh." Her lashes came up, and he saw the moment when they hesitated, her eyes focused on the swollen evidence of the desire he'd tried to smother since he'd first opened his eyes to her. Then she raised her gaze to his face, two patches of high color in her cheeks the only sign of her awareness of his condition.

"You...have to be sure," he said tightly. "I...can't make any promises about stopping. Not now. Not anymore." He took a breath, then let it out. "I want you too much."

She stood up then, not touching him, even though they were bare inches apart. "You have to be sure, too." She sounded a little breathless. "I never meant to... I didn't realize what I was doing to you. Not that," she said at the wry twist of his lips. "I mean...I don't want you to feel..."

She paused, biting her lip. When she went on, her voice was strong and steady. "I'm a big girl, Con. I make my own decisions and take the consequences. If you can't believe that, if you're going to feel guilty, then it's not right."

He looked down at her with an expression of mingled amusement and exasperation. "If you're changing your mind, you picked a hell of a time."

"Don't joke, Con." She refused to be swayed. "I won't put you through that, too, on top of what I've already done."

"Now who's feeling guilty?" His voice was soft, warm, almost a caress.

"I am," she answered honestly. "I didn't realize—"

"Do you realize you're driving me crazy? That I don't care about anything anymore except that if you don't kiss me I'm going to jump ship and look for the nearest shark?"

Shiloh wasn't conscious of moving; she knew only that the inches between them vanished. She was up against the hard wall of his chest, and his arms were tight around her. The damp cloth of her swimsuit might as well be nonexistent; she could feel every hard, muscled inch of him, and the thin barrier of the nylon shorts did nothing to restrain the surging hardness she felt pressed against her thigh.

She lifted her head, lips parted for breath; there suddenly didn't seem to be enough air in this open, airy place. When she looked up at him, she saw his nostrils flare as if he, too, were feeling the lack. Then such a minor thing as breathing faded into insignificance as his mouth came down on hers.

All the urgency, all the need he had been suppressing were poured into that kiss, and Shiloh shivered with its intensity. She could taste the salt of the sea on his lips, and then only him, only the hot, wonderful taste of him. His hands slid up to cup her face, to tilt her head back as his tongue plunged forward into the honeyed warmth of her mouth. And she met him hungrily, her mouth seeking, wanting, her hands lifting to lock behind his neck, to hold him close.

She heard the low sound he made, a rumbling groan that came from deep within his chest. His mouth left hers, but before she could draw breath to protest a tiny gasp escaped her as his lips traced a fiery path along her cheek to her ear.

She could feel the warmth of his breath, and it sent a shiver through her. He felt it, and his arms tightened around her. The shiver rippled through her again, stronger this time, when she felt the tip of his tongue lightly trace the curve of her ear. Her hands went to his shoulders, her fingers digging into hard muscle. He circled the sensitive opening lightly, delicately, and her fingers tightened as a small, breathy moan broke from her.

Suddenly he stopped, pulling her tight against him, pressing her head to his chest with a hand that was oddly unsteady. He leaned down to lay his cheek against the damp silk of her hair.

"Con?" She heard him draw in a breath, but he didn't speak. "If you ask me once more if I'm sure, I'll push you overboard."

The rumble came from low and deep in his chest, and when he laughed she thought she'd never heard such a wonderful sound. No more, she promised herself. He wasn't going to keep it locked away anymore.

And then, in one swift movement, he swept her up into his arms. She wasn't sure how he managed to get down the narrow stairway to the cabin, but by then his lips had claimed hers again and she didn't care. She supposed she should spare a thought for the fact that he was carrying her toward an irreversible moment in her life, but she was so certain deep down in her heart that it was right that it didn't matter; all she felt was eagerness.

He carried her to her bunk, sweeping aside clothes and blankets with the arm that had been supporting her shoulders before she locked her arms around his neck. His lips were alternately hot and demanding, then soft and coaxing, but always sending growing ripples of flame along nerves that had discovered a new function. He laid her down with exquisite care, his mouth never leaving hers.

Somehow the knowledge that this time would be different, that this time it would not end in hurt, angry frustration, added fuel to the fire he was kindling within her. She clung to him as he lay down beside her, wanting him closer, wanting to hurry even as she wanted this to go on and on. Her head was whirling, and only when she felt the long, naked length of him against her, felt the unfettered strength and heat of him, hot and swollen against her, did she know that he had peeled off the damp shorts.

He trailed little kisses down her neck, lingering at the hollow where her pulse was beginning to beat wildly. His mouth moved downward over silken skin to the rise of her breast, teasing with those little feathery kisses.

She couldn't bear it, she thought. Already her breasts felt swollen and heavy, her nipples taut and aching for him. The memory of how his mouth had felt on her leapt like a living thing along her sizzling nerves, and, helpless to stop herself, she lifted her hand to press his head to her.

As if he'd been waiting for that sign he moved quickly, reaching for the narrow straps of the shimmering green swimsuit. He began to slide them off her slender shoulders, and she wriggled eagerly to help him, rolling the damp fabric down and kicking it away, baring herself to his heated gaze, trembling a little in her shyness.

He groaned, his hands trembling slightly as he reached for her. He cupped the full, soft flesh of her breasts in his palms, lifting the silken weight, and with a convulsive movement he buried his face in the valley between those lush curves.

"Shiloh," he murmured against her skin. "I've wanted this ever since I woke up and found the tomboy I expected had turned into the most incredible woman I've ever known."

Her shyness vanished. She threaded slender fingers through the dark, heavy silk of his hair.

"I've wanted it all my life. Even when I wasn't sure you existed. I'm so glad I didn't have to wait forever."

She realized her words were rather cryptic, but when he lifted his head and she looked into blue eyes darkened with passion, she knew he'd understood. She reached for him, her mouth hungry for the taste of his once more, but he shifted suddenly, raising himself up on his elbows. When he spoke there was a compelling note in his voice.

"I don't want to hurry, not now, not...your first time, but I don't know how long I can hold out. It's been a long time." He wet his lips. "Just let me..."

He couldn't finish, and his head dropped to her breast with a ragged moan. Eagerly he sought her nipple, catching it between gentle teeth and flicking it with his tongue. He licked away the salty taste, and when he had reached the sweetness beneath, he closed his lips around the taut peak and suckled deeply.

She gasped at the hot, searing pleasure that shot through her, arching involuntarily as her aching flesh begged for more. The feel of her supple body lifting for him, offering her breasts to him, sent a glowing, molten shaft of heat ripping through him. His hands clenched, knotting into fists as he fought for control.

He wasn't going to make it. He knew it as surely as he knew that he'd never tasted anything as sweet as the tight little crest that was rising to his tongue. The next time she moved like that, the next time she made it so achingly, sweetly clear that she wanted him, it was going to be all over. He was no better than some fumbling teenager who'd just discovered sex, and he was going to last about that long.

He clenched his jaw fiercely. He *would* hold out, damn it. She was giving him a gift beyond price, something more precious than anything he'd ever been given in his life, and he wasn't going to spoil it for her. He'd never been with anyone so innocently inexperienced, only with women who knew exactly what they wanted, just as he did: fleeting physical gratification with no strings attached. Although he hadn't wanted the responsibility, he was beyond stopping now. But he would make it good for her, and if he died in the process, so be it.

With an effort that made sweat pop out on his forehead, made every muscle in his body ripple in protest, he fought down the pulsing, demanding urge to bury himself in her and ease his throbbing need. With a slowness that spoke of tight control rather than an intentional building of anticipation, he lifted his head and moved to her other breast.

Swept up by the storm of new, unexpected sensations, Shiloh was unaware of his struggle. Every nerve was overloaded, sending rapid-fire bursts of pleasure to every part of her, radiating out from the rigid peak that had found a home in the wet heat of his mouth. She had no room for anything but growing awe at what she was feeling, at what her body was capable of. For him. Only for him. She knew somehow, in that hidden part of her that had lain dormant for so long, that part of her had waited for him even while she doubted his existence.

Con shifted to his side, keeping one leg thrown over her, trying to ignore the silken caress of her thigh against his rigid, throbbing flesh. He drew her eager nipple deeper into his mouth as his hand slid down over her slender rib cage, lingering, stroking the smooth satin of her stomach. He tugged with his lips, teased with his tongue, at that taut crest while his hand circled, petted, caressed her silken skin. He felt the moment when she began to move again, her hips lifting to his hand, and smothered a shuddering groan against the soft, full curve of her breast.

When she felt his hand move, slipping down her body until his fingers tangled in the reddish curls at the top of her thighs, Shiloh tensed instinctively. But then an older, much stronger instinct took over, and she parted her thighs eagerly for his touch.

"Oh, Shiloh," he murmured as his fingers reached her smooth, ready warmth. She heard him but was too caught up in her own revelations to do anything except marvel at her body's response.

She felt, with a shuddering intensity that rippled through every part of her, the first delicate touch of his fingers inside her tender flesh. She knew by the way he touched her, by the way his caress was so smooth, so easy, that she was slickly wet, and she shivered in wonder at how completely her body was readying itself for him.

The very fact of that readiness nearly shattered the tenuous grip Con had on what was left of his tattered control. The moment his probing fingers had found her wet, her body waiting for him, that slick heat beckoning, it had taken every ounce of self-discipline he'd ever had to restrain himself. His mind was fighting his body, and with each innocent movement she made, each indication that she was as eager for him as he was for her, the haze of pleasure clouded his mind a little more, leaving less to fight the battle he didn't want to win in the first place.

She was writhing now, her hips undulating in time with his caress, her face a mask of awed disbelief at the sensations he was drawing from that untouched center that had come pulsingly alive beneath his touch. Her breath was coming in quick, desperate gasps, every other one a soft, ragged moan. She clutched at him, her eyes widening as the heat from his mouth, which had returned once more to her swollen breast, streaked downward to join with the fire erupting beneath his fingers. She was arching, striving, mindless to anything except that he was pushing her to the very edge of bearable sensation.

"Con!"

"I know," he whispered, pausing in his words to move to her other breast and suck fiercely, wringing another gasp from her. "Go with it, Green-eyes."

The sight of her, her eyes full of the shock of what she was feeling, her body dancing to his touch, gave him back the determination he'd nearly lost. That he could do this for her, that he could shatter that unnatural control of hers, filled him with a new resolve that he would wait, he would somehow hold on. He had to hold on, because he knew with certainty that his inflamed body would not wait once he was inside her, that the moment he was sheathed in the slick, wet heat he had touched, he would be lost.

She cried out once more and bucked wildly beneath his hand. He never stopped that circling, massaging caress, but he lifted his head, seized with an irresistible need to watch it happen for her, this first time.

He had expected it to be erotic, to drive him to the brink of sanity, to make the need to drive himself into her silken heat unbearable, but he had never expected that watching her in that most vulnerable of moments would make him feel so utterly and completely humble.

And then she was there, her eyes hot with passion and surprise as her body reached the precipice and went flying over. She cried out his name as the spasms took her, a hot, sweet shivering sound from deep in her throat. It sent an echoing ripple that caught him by surprise, and it took every remnant of his control to stop himself from following her over the edge right then. He groaned, beyond being embarrassed at his own failings where she was concerned.

He wanted to wait, to let her savor it, but the sound of his name in that tone of amazement, of delight, of glorious pleasure, shattered his fragile control into splinters. He moved over her, dreading that moment when he knew he would have to hurt her, but unable to stop. He only hoped that now, when the echoes of pleasure were still pulsing through her, the pain would be less.

When she felt the first touch of his hardened flesh between her thighs, Shiloh looked up at him through lowered lashes, too languorous to move. He'd wanted it that way, she realized with the first glimpse of his face; even drawn tight with need, his concern for her was plain.

A surge of tenderness swept over her, so strong that, coming on the heels of the incredible sensations she'd just experienced, it left her breathless. Only now did she realize the meaning of the strain in his face, the rigid tautness of his muscles as he had gently, sweetly shown her the way. Only now did she realize how much he had held back for her sake, and what it had cost him.

"Please," she whispered, her hands going to cup his face, her legs lifting instinctively to caress his lean hips.

With a harsh, strangled cry he moved, his hardened shaft probing the wet heat he had created in her. He had eased his own way, and she opened for him eagerly. He nearly cried out again at that first touch, astounded that the sensations could be so intense when he had barely begun, had not even breached that final, thin barrier.

He tried to go slow, hoping to spare her some of the inevitable pain, but her hands slid down to his waist, then his hips, and she urged him forward. His body, strained to the point of shattering into a million pieces, surrendered to her silent entreaty, and he thrust forward.

He felt the resistance, then felt it yield, felt her slender body tense beneath him as she bit back a cry. Then he was inside her, surrounded by searing, gripping heat, and he couldn't stop the gasp of pleasure that escaped him. He had thought that once he was sheathed by that giving yet clasping flesh he would find it impossible to be still; now he doubted if he could move. She was so hot, so tight; impossibly, he could feel himself growing even harder inside her.

Her languor forgotten, Shiloh stared up at him in awed wonder. The pain had been sharp, tearing, but it had eased to a dull ache that faded to insignificance beside the incredible feel of his body inside hers. She knew now what that hollowness, that aching longing for something she couldn't name, had been. It was this, this wonderful, astonishing fullness, this sense of completeness she'd never felt before, that she had been yearning for.

Instinctively she moved, shifting her hips, wanting to know, to feel, every inch of him. Just that slight movement of welcome sent him careening out of control and he had to move.

He knew with his first thrust that he would have to surrender any thought of taking her with him this time. He was too close to the edge already; it had been too long, and he wanted her too much. He tried to go easy, afraid of hurting her, but she rose to meet him on the next thrust, and he had to abandon that thought, as well.

He cast off all thought. He was a mass of sizzling, crackling nerves, centered on the incredible sensations she was causing in him, a mindless, driven thing whose field of vision had narrowed to the soft, loving woman who was holding him, taking him into herself in fierce, hot welcome.

He had left all his experience far behind the moment he had slipped into that scorching heat. At the first sliding caress of her body he had surpassed anything he'd ever felt, and he knew this was what he'd really been fighting; he'd known it would be like this. And he'd known what it would mean, having tasted the extraordinary sweetness of this, to go back to the cold, dim world he lived in.

Then he felt her move again, those long, golden legs lifting with his thrust, the taut, silken thighs sliding over his skin from waist to hips and back. A choking cry ripped from him, and he drove forward, hard and deep, unable to hold back another second. And at the depth of that long, piercing stroke he exploded into her, pulse after surging, boiling pulse, each with a force that left him shaken, drained, weak.

"Shy," he whispered as he collapsed atop her, every muscle quivering. "Oh, Shy."

He buried his face in the curve of her shoulder, aware that he was still shaking but unable to stop. Nor could he move to relieve her of his weight, although her arms were still wrapped tightly around him, holding him close, as if she liked the feel of him on her.

And in her, he thought, vividly aware that he was still embedded deep inside her sleek, supple body. Little echoes of that eruption of pleasure skated along nerves he would have thought too scorched to carry them.

At last, when his breathing began to slow, and his hammering heart eased back toward its normal rhythm, he managed to get his elbows under him and raise himself up. "I'm sorry," he whispered. "I couldn't wait."

Shiloh lifted one long, slender finger and pressed it to his lips, hushing him. She didn't speak, just shook her head, letting the look of awe and tenderness that was shining in her face be her answer. He ducked his head, pressing his lips gently to her neck, hugging her slender shoulders fiercely.

In truth, she couldn't speak. She couldn't find words to say what she was feeling. She couldn't begin to tell him how he had made her feel, what it meant to her to know that he had felt the same. She had never thought herself capable of such an incredible, soaring flight, yet he had sent her spiraling upward until her world had exploded into heat and light and pleasure.

And she knew she could never tell him how she had felt looking up at him in those final seconds, seeing his face so tightly drawn with passion and pleasure, his blue eyes free at last of that haunted, shadowed look, and knowing that she had given him that.

And most of all for the cry that had burst from him even as he burst inside her, her name in that ragged, fevered voice, telling her that he had never forgotten who it was he held. And the sound of her name, that nickname that was suddenly, unexpectedly precious, the name he had whispered once in the grips of a fever of a different kind, that still echoed in her ears with a honeyed sweetness that warmed her to her soul.

She slid one hand down his back, over the long, hard ridges of muscle, loving the incredible feel of sleek skin beneath her fingers. The other hand crept to the back of his head to press him to her as she twined her fingers in his damp, thick hair.

He shivered as her fingers brushed the back of his neck, and his hands tightened where he gripped her shoulders. She felt the hot, feathery caress of his breath as he pressed his lips to her skin. As if of its own volition, her other hand went to the small of his back, pressing downward, as if to hold him there, cradled against her hips.

That slight, tentative pressure sent white-hot fire surging along nerves that, instead of being charred by that violent eruption, seemed now to have multiplied, to have expanded until the slightest brush of her skin against his made his whole body sizzle.

He lifted his head a fraction, trailing his lips along the side of her neck, aware that he was surging to life inside her once more. He knew it was more than just the long months of celibacy, that even if he'd been carousing around for months before, she would still have this effect on him.

Shiloh felt the change, felt him begin to harden, to expand, to offer her that glorious fullness once again, and she drew an eager little breath. He raised his head then, his eyes full of desire tinged with amusement. She saw the glint of humor and blushed.

"I...didn't know...so soon...I thought it took longer." She flushed as she floundered in unfamiliar territory.

He grinned. "I'd like to say I'm that good, but I'm afraid it's just abstinence." His voice became softer, and his grin faded. "And you."

Shiloh felt a swelling tightness in her chest that made it hard to breathe for a moment. She felt a stinging behind her eyelids and lowered them quickly, afraid that if she looked any longer into the warmth of his eyes she would be lost to tears. And that he would read in her eyes what she couldn't tell him, not yet. She knew that the last thing he would want to hear right now was that the naive young woman whose virginity he had just taken was in love with him.

But she was, she thought as he lowered his head to trail his mouth over her skin. She loved him, all of him, the dark shadows and the too rare brightness, loved him with a power that frightened her, because it was so strong, so soon.

And she was, she thought with a last, rueful flash of sanity as his mouth reached her breast, most definitely naive. She had scoffed, albeit in tactful silence, at her friends' tales of woe about their current passions, consigning such things to the realm of make-believe. Proud of her self-control, she had told herself they were in love with the idea of love, not the pale reality. She had been smug, condescending—and utterly, completely wrong.

Then his mouth found her nipple, taut and ready, and any rational thought fled. She knew only the feel of his mouth on her tight, swollen flesh, the feel of him hard and deep inside her. Yes, she had been wrong, so wrong, and she'd never been more glad about being so mistaken.

Con was determined to go slowly this time, knowing this was new to her. But the very tightness that reminded him of that was also driving him to the brink of madness; how could she be so small and yet take him so deep? She surrounded him, caressed him, seared him with her inner flame, until he was so hard and aching that he groaned aloud against her breast.

As if fired by that involuntary sound, Shiloh began to move, to shift her hips under him, wanting all of him so deeply inside her that he would never be gone from her. The groan came again, harsher, huskier, and he began to move.

With long, slow thrusts that made her shudder he stroked the very core of her, each time pushing her higher, building the heat inside her until she was writhing beneath him. Any pain her body was feeling at the unaccustomed invasion was lost in the smoke of the inferno he was feeding. Again and again he thrust, until she was a writhing, undulating mass of sheer sensation, uttering soft little cries. She had turned to quivering, molten liquid in his arms, aware only that if it wasn't for those arms she would lose the boundary of her body and go flying away.

And then she did go flying, his last fierce thrust sending her spiraling out into whirling, brilliant space, aware only of an odd, gasping cry that coalesced into his name, not even knowing that the cry came from her.

Con felt her nails digging into his back and revelled in it. He felt the first ripple of her muscles, the shudder that came as her body tightened, gripping his.

"Yes," he gasped, barely aware of saying it aloud, "oh, yes, Green-eyes, that's it."

And then he was with her, drawn by the incredible stroking of her hot, rippling flesh, his head thrown back as her name came bursting from him as he met her heat with his own.

Shiloh didn't think she would ever come back to earth, and she didn't care. Her body, her senses, her very soul, were soaring, singing out her joy. Her entire world had narrowed to this time and this man, and she knew she would be content to stay here forever.

He shifted as if to leave her, and she made a little sound of protest, hugging him close. His head came up, and he looked at her, his eyes troubled.

"I'm too heavy for you." She shook her head fiercely. He let out a long breath, then swallowed heavily. "Did I hurt you a lot?" He knew he had; he remembered that moment when he had first entered her and she had held back a cry of pain.

"Only for a moment." She looked up at him through the thick fringe of her lashes, the corners of her mouth twitching oddly. "I barely noticed."

"I wish—" he began penitently, then stopped when she smiled. It was a teasing, sassy smile, a Cheshire cat smile that lit up her green eyes joyously. Then she giggled. He had never heard her giggle, never expected to. Taken aback, he gaped at her.

"Oh, Con!"

She lifted a hand to cup his face. She doubted if he would understand all that he had done for her, all the doubts he had erased as if they'd never been, the certainty he had given her of her own capacity to love and give, the knowledge that her drive for control had not destroyed the woman inside her.

"You look so serious, so worried, and I feel so wonderful!"

Something warm and visceral expanded inside him, something he'd never felt before. Convulsively he hugged her, and before he could put a name to the oddly unsettling emotion, he almost blurted it out.

"Shiloh, I—"

He broke off, realizing in shock that he had been about to tell her that he loved her. My God, he thought numbly, burying his face once more in the smooth curve at the base of her neck. He had thought her beautiful from the first moment he'd seen her, had quickly come to respect and admire her courage and intelligence, had wanted her with an urgent, unceasing need that he'd never experienced in his life, but until now he hadn't added it all up to the incontrovertible total.

This revelation, attacking emotions already raw from the incredible pleasure she had given him, was more than he could deal with right now. It couldn't be. What the hell did he know about love, anyway?

He slid off her, rolling over onto his back. Of its own volition, his arm tightened around her, bringing her with him to nestle close to his side. She lay quietly for a long time; then, slowly, her hand slid across his chest.

She traced the faint, white line that he'd told her was from a knife. Her fingers paused at the point where the scar ended over his breastbone, trembling slightly with the sudden, unexpected urge that had swept her; she wanted to kill whoever had done this to him. It was the fierce, protective instinct of a tigress, primitive and basic, and it made her eyes glow with its intensity.

"Did he pay for this?" she asked softly.

Startled, Con stared at her. He searched her face for censure, for distaste, and found only that urgent glow that called out to some primal element in him, an element that was closer to the surface in him than in most men.

"Yes," he said finally, his voice oddly soft as he watched her.

"Good."

He let out a long, quiet breath. Even this, he thought. Even this she accepted, not with the peculiar, almost perverted fascination some women had with men who lived the kind of life he did, but with the quiet acknowledgment of a debt paid, of a balance kept. In some hidden part of his mind that he wouldn't even admit was there, a check mark went up, the latest in a long row as she once more surprised him, once more failed to act as he'd come to expect all women to act.

Shiloh gave the thin scar a last, gentle touch, still a little astonished at her own reaction. She had for so long fought what she thought was overprotectiveness from first her father, then her brother, and now she suddenly understood a little better how they had felt. And why. It was just further proof of how deeply she had fallen in love with this dark, solitary man.

Con shivered under her feather-light touch. He might not know anything about love, but he'd learned a hell of a lot about wanting in the last five days.

He couldn't afford to want, he thought sharply. Not this, not her, not when he never knew if he would see the sun rise tomorrow. And just when the hell did you ever get what you want, anyway, McQuade? he asked himself bitterly. Acid rose in him, stinging, blistering. It was not a familiar feeling; he rarely indulged in feeling sorry for himself.

You should be worried about her, not yourself, he lectured himself severely. But she would be all right. She was strong, tough, and she knew how things were in his work. She knew that as soon as this was over, he would be gone. She knew it, had known it all along, and still had made her choice. She would be all right. He had to believe that. He couldn't live with knowing that he had hurt the person who had given him the only patch of true sunlight he'd ever had in his life.

Then she stirred in his arms, her heavily lashed eyes lifting dreamily to his, a warm glow kindling in their depths while a small smile curved her soft mouth. His heart turned over in his chest, and his arms tightened around her involuntarily.

How could he give this up? How could he go on, knowing this was possible and yet waking every day to emptiness instead of the warmth of her? For the first time he regretted what he had done, for no other reason than the hell he had condemned himself to for the rest of his life.

Then she turned her head to press a soft, gentle kiss on his shoulder, the touch of her lips sending little tendrils of heat spiraling outward, and he knew it was worth any price. He only hoped he could still believe that when all he had were memories to keep him warm.

Chapter 11

Later, when she paused in fixing more hot chocolate to press a slender palm just below her navel, he felt a flood of that old remorse. Had he hurt her? He must have, he thought, getting quickly to his feet. He'd been much too rough with her; he'd driven too hard, too deep, for her tender, innocent body.

"Shy?" he whispered, going to stand close beside her, trying to find the words to ask how much damage he'd done. She turned to look up at him, her eyes wide with wonder, and her words seared his remorse to ashes.

"Sometimes...it's like I can still feel you inside me...like you never really left me."

Groaning low in his throat he pulled her into his arms, marveling at how this guileless woman could send his senses reeling and make his body ache with just a few short, innocently awestruck words.

Much later, the chocolate cold and forgotten in the mugs on the counter, Shiloh lay in the bunk looking up at him. She lifted one slender finger to run it around the curve of his ear and down the strong line of his jaw. He shivered, and the dark semicircles of his lashes lifted.

"We shouldn't have done that," he said ruefully. "You're going to be awfully sore."

"I have a lot of years to make up for," she said cheerfully, ignoring the fact that he was right; she was sore already.

"You don't have to do it all in one day."

Don't I? she thought, running her hand over the smooth, hot silk of his chest. Don't I have to take as much as I can now, while I have you, before you turn around and walk out of my life? Because you will, won't you? Even though I love you.

Shiloh lowered her head quickly, afraid he would see in her eyes what she knew she had to conceal. She could not, would not, tie him to her that way, and she knew him well enough to know that she could. He already felt guilty enough, responsible enough, at having taken, no matter how freely it had been offered, her virginity; if he knew the naive little girl he thought she was had fallen in love with him, she might as well slap a shackle on him. And while she might be naive, she wasn't so naive as to think that would work.

Nor was she naive enough to think that he loved her just because he had made love to her so passionately, so sweetly. There was a world of difference between desire and love, and she didn't try to fool herself into thinking the one was the other. No matter how much it hurt. No, she told herself firmly, Connor McQuade was a solitary man, and only he could make the decision to change that; she couldn't do it for him. And she held only the slimmest of hopes that he could—or would—do it himself.

A chill that went beyond the briskness of fall overtook them as the sun disappeared below the horizon. Shiloh shivered as she began to close up the ports before turning on the heater again. Rather than drain the batteries she lit the kerosene lamps, preferring the soft, golden glow, anyway.

When she was done, she returned to the galley, where Con was chopping the solitary potato they had to add it to the pot of clam chowder on the stove. Her stomach growled unexpectedly, and she couldn't help smiling. Lovemaking, it seemed, worked up quite an appetite.

She watched him cut the potato with quick, sure strokes, watched his strong, supple hands with an avid pleasure that surprised her. She got as much pleasure, although a different kind, out of watching those long, competent fingers as she did watching the flex of taut muscle in his arms and shoulders, or looking at the flat, muscled ridges of his belly.

Watching those hands made her think of what they could do when they turned to her, stroking, caressing, firing nerves she knew with certainty had never been there before. Her body began to catch fire at the mere thought; her palms itched and her fingers curled with the need to touch him, to feel those taut muscles ripple beneath her hands, to feel his body surge to pulsing life.

"Damn." Her eyes shot to his face at his whispered curse. "Stop looking at me like that."

"Like what?"

"Like I'm dinner," he grated, "and you're starved."

She colored, embarrassed that her thoughts had been so obvious. "Oh," she said, blushing. But a tiny smile curved her mouth, and it sent a dart of fire through him.

He groaned and purposely turned his back to her, stirring the chowder with a much more forceful hand than was necessary. God, he thought. He'd made love to her, and she to him, until they could barely stand up, until her delicate flesh was bruised, and still he was ready to take her again, right here and now, on the damned table if he could get that far. His jaw clenched, and he bit his lip fiercely until he regained some semblance of control.

The soup was good, although Con had to keep beating down the images brought on by her earlier words as she had pressed her hand to her body as if she indeed could still feel him there. He wondered if there was the slightest chance he could keep his hands off her tonight, giving her a chance to heal a little. If she would just cooperate, quit looking at him like that, quit touching him . . . Sure, McQuade, he sighed inwardly. He sipped at his soup glumly.

When, after they had cleared the table, she went to the radio to call her father, he toyed with the idea of going above to give her some privacy. But she'd given no indication that she minded his being there, and it was awfully chilly out there.... He compromised by picking up one of the books from the shelf above the settee and at least appearing to be engrossed as the call went through.

"Hello."

Con heard her sharp intake of breath and looked up. Although a little brusque, it had been her father's voice; he'd heard it enough now to know. Yet she had gone pale, her fingers tightening around the microphone until her knuckles were white. He closed the book.

"Is this . . . The Hat Shop?"

She sounded oddly breathless, and Con got to his feet.

"No." That same brusque tone. "This is 555-1700. Their number is 1704." There was a rustle of sound, something muttered in the background, unintelligible. "Excuse me, I have to go."

The line went dead, and Shiloh stood staring at the mike clutched in her hand. She had gone waxen, her green eyes filling with horror. His stomach knotting and his heart beginning to pound, Con crossed the salon of the boat in one long stride. He gripped her shoulders and turned her to look at him, heedless that she'd dropped the microphone.

"What is it?"

"They're there." Her voice was harsh, a raspy, broken whisper.

"What?" He looked at her with a disbelief that faded before the look in her eyes. If he had learned anything about Shiloh Reese in these past days, it was that she usually had a pretty good reason for anything she said or did. If she said they were there, they were. "How do you know?"

In the small part of her mind that wasn't stunned into numbness, Shiloh registered that he had accepted that she knew and was only questioning how. He trusted her that far, at least.

"For as long as I can remember, my father has never answered the phone 'hello.'"

Con's brow furrowed, then cleared. "'Yo,'" he whispered in sudden understanding.

Shiloh nodded. "He's always answered like that. Always 'yo.' 'Hello' was saved as a red flag, a warning no one else would know."

"And 'The Hat Shop'?" he asked tensely, fearing he already knew the answer.

"The black hats are there."

"Damn."

Con swore softly, bitterly, as he released her shoulders. He didn't waste time on apologies; they would be meaningless now, and he didn't know any words to express how rotten he felt, anyway. He started to reach for her again but stopped, thinking that he was the last person she would want to touch her now, now that he had managed to get her father into this as deeply as she was.

"What . . . what will they do?" The tremor in her usually cool, unshakable voice as she sank down on the chair at the navigation station told him more than he wanted to know about her state of mind. He looked at her, saw the fear in her eyes, and thought about what he should say.

"The truth, Con."

He sighed. Of course. No sugarcoating things for Shiloh Reese. "They know we've got to surface sometime. And that you'll contact him sooner or later. And then they've got their lever."

"But what good would getting to me through my father do them?"

"Because they know you're with me."

"But why would they think you would care? I mean, they don't know . . ." Her words trailed off as she blushed. He nearly smiled at her until he saw the touch of doubt that had crept into her eyes.

"I care," he said suddenly, fiercely.

Thankfully, he saw the doubt fade in the instant before she looked down at the deck beneath their feet. "But they don't know that," she said in a tiny voice.

"If they knew enough to connect me to you in the first place," he said, still angry because he couldn't begin to figure out how they had come up with that particular piece of information, "they may think there's a connection between me and . . . the Reeses in general."

She looked up at him then, a tender warmth glowing in her eyes, as if she were hoping that he, too, thought there was a connection between him and all the Reeses. It startled him; at the least he'd expected anger because he'd gotten her father into danger, but there was none. Only that tempting warmth. It lured him even as he reminded himself coldly that it was impossible.

"It doesn't matter what they think," he said, his voice a little sharp with the chill of his last thought, "or how they made the connection. Not right now."

He reached down for the radio mike she'd dropped. He'd never used a radiotelephone before, but he'd watched her—all too closely—enough to know how it worked, and he soon had the marine operator. He knew Sam probably wasn't back yet, but he had to at least try. He didn't like giving out Sam's private number over a radio line, but he didn't have much choice.

"WestCorp."

"Julia." His answer to Sam's quietly efficient secretary of ten years was a sigh of resignation. She only answered this line if Sam himself was gone.

"Con?"

"Yeah. He's not back yet, is he." His flat tone made it a statement instead of a question.

"No. I spoke to him yesterday. He won't return until late tomorrow night." He let out a long, tired breath. "Con, is something wrong?"

"You could say that." His jaw tightened. "If you talk to him again, tell him . . . tell him I had to go ahead."

"All right." She asked no questions, and not for the first time Con was grateful for the woman's unswerving loyalty. "Is there anything we can do?"

"We?"

"Joe or I."

"I thought Joe was on vacation."

"I didn't think you knew the word, you who haven't taken a day off in seven years." A soft laugh came through the small speaker. "He was, but he said he got bored."

A chill was beginning somewhere at the base of Con's spine. "When . . . did he come back?"

"Last week."

The chill became a frost. "When?"

"You mean, what day exactly?" She sounded puzzled, but once more didn't ask any questions. "Let me look—" there was the sound of a computer keyboard being used "—here it is, he came back on Tuesday."

The frost became ice, hard, unyielding and utterly frigid.

"Yes, that's right," Julia went on, "because I was here late catching up on some data-entry work and in walked Joe. He's here in his office now. Do you want to talk to him?"

"No." His voice was flat, inflectionless. "And don't tell him I called, Julia."

There was a pause. "Well, of course, if you say so," she said, surprise obvious in her voice.

"It's important, Julia. Not a word."

"Certainly." The businesslike tone was back. "Anything else?"

"Just tell Sam not to do anything until he hears from me. Anything," he repeated emphatically.

"I will." For just a moment her demeanor slipped. "Are you all right, Con?"

"Sure. Just great." He heard the echo of his biting tone. "Sorry, Julia. Things are unraveling a bit here. Tell Sam I'll get in touch when I can."

Shiloh watched him hang up the mike, saw the bleakness that had come over his face and the frost that had returned to his eyes. It tore at her and, for the moment at least, transcended the realization that had come to her during his conversation; he had given the great Sam West an order, and in the tone of one who knew it would be obeyed. But now all she could do was ache for him as she saw that implacable mask descend again. He was once again the grim-faced man she had first met.

Finally she asked softly, "Joe?"

His eyes closed, he swallowed heavily, then took a long, deep breath. "It has to be," he said. "It's the only thing that fits. He's got the access and the resources."

"And they came after you the morning after he came back."

He nodded slowly. "You were right. They didn't know about me at first. Until Joe got back to tell them." He laughed harshly. "He always joked about retiring to some private, tropical island. Apparently it wasn't a joke."

"Are you sure?"

He let out a harsh breath. "He came up with reasons to go to Switzerland at least twice a year. He does a good job—" his lips twisted wryly "—so Sam never questioned it. He figured he just wanted to sneak in some skiing." He ran a hand wearily through his tousled hair. "I still don't know how he found out about you. He couldn't have known Linc and I had any contact after the Philippines. Not even Sam knew."

"Does it matter now?"

"No," he muttered. He straightened up then, his voice taking on that sharp, ordering tone she hadn't heard since they boarded the boat. "What's the next closest port?"

She didn't comment on the obvious assumption that they didn't dare go back to Dana Point, merely asked, "Which way?"

"North."

She knew then that he meant to go to her father. "Con... you said they won't hurt him while they need him—"

"What's closest?" he interrupted.

"You said they couldn't use a lever if they couldn't find you. I could go—"

"And give them you to use on me? Not a chance. Now, what's next going north?"

She wondered if he even realized what he'd said, what he'd admitted with his harsh words. And she wondered even more at how quickly she had reached the point of becoming as worried about him as she was about her father.

"But you said—"

"I talk too damned much."

She couldn't stop her eyebrows from shooting upward at the absurdity of that.

"Around you," he amended, a little abashed despite the grimness that had returned to his expression. Then the sharpness was back in his voice. "We're wasting time."

"Newport," she said succinctly.

"How long?"

"If we push and we're lucky, four-and-a-half to five hours. There are emergency docks at the harbor department. We could tie up there for a while, but I'm not sure how long they let you stay."

"Long enough, the way this is unraveling," he said grimly.

She paled a little but nodded, and he could have kicked himself for his caustic words. He opened his mouth to speak, but she merely said they'd best get started and reached for her jacket. Tugging it on, she headed for the hatchway. One foot on the steps, she looked back over her shoulder at him.

"I'm sorry about Joe," she said softly. "I know you . . . trusted him." Then she disappeared into the cockpit.

Con stared after her, stunned. He had gotten her into the middle of this mess, had practically dragged her into bed with him, and now had managed to endanger her crippled father into the bargain, and she was sorry for him because someone he'd trusted had turned traitor on him?

He laughed under his breath, harsh and strained. It had been so long since he'd trusted anyone, he couldn't even remember when he'd come to expect betrayal as the rule and not the exception. He didn't know what it was like to take anyone at face value anymore. Yet he trusted her, as he trusted her brother. . . .

And she trusted him. Enough so that she was worried about him as well as her father. And that scared the hell out of him. Don't, Shy, he thought painfully. Don't trust me.

I'll let you down.... I'm not like you. I don't have the blood, not like you and Linc, you know who you are—

His thoughts were cut off by the sound of the diesel firing up, and he scrambled toward the hatch to head for the anchor winch. When they were under way and Shiloh assured him that she would call him if she needed help, he went below and began to search for something to write on.

Shiloh thanked the young sheriff's deputy again. He grinned, and, after looking her up and down admiringly once more, he threw Con an envious look and drove off.

"You're awfully damned good at this," Con grumbled.

He was somehow a little disgruntled at how easy it had been. One look from those big green eyes and a few words about her ailing father and how she had to get to him as soon as possible, and they had the *Phoenix* secured at a county dock and, in a manner of speaking, a uniformed chauffeur.

"Well, it was the truth. And it worked, didn't it?"

He couldn't argue with that. He'd wanted a place that was full of people even at this hour; the airport filled the bill admirably. "Yeah. But did you have to flirt with him all the way up here?"

"I was not flirting with him!" She glared at Con. "I was merely polite. It was the least I could do. He was giving us a ride, after all. I'm sure he has to deal with enough rude people as it is."

He muttered something unintelligible, then took her arm and guided her down the sidewalk away from the terminal. Shiloh went along meekly enough, warmed in spite of herself by the fact that her supposed flirting had angered him.

They paused only to find an Express Mail mailbox, where Con deposited whatever he'd written on their return from the island. Shiloh knew only that it was addressed to a post office box in Denver; there had been no name on the envelope. Then they walked past the long, glass-domed, Quonset-shaped terminal building that had been recently finished and headed toward the parking lot. He was carrying her nylon suitcase, along with the big canvas bag; they could easily have just gotten off a plane. Which was exactly what he wanted, she realized; no one gave them a second glance as they went into the long-term parking lot.

They had trudged down an entire row of the lot, Con carefully eyeing each vehicle, before it dawned on her. Her eyes widened, and she stopped in her tracks to stare at him.

"Oh, no," she began.

"No choice," he said shortly, not bothering to deny it. The iceberg was back in command, she thought, and the softer, gentler, happier man she'd seen at the island had vanished as if he'd never been.

Suddenly he stopped next to a rather nondescript blue sedan a couple of years old. He reached out to try the door, but stopped abruptly and moved on.

"Excuse me," she said sweetly, "I don't have much experience in the finer points of auto theft, but what was wrong with that one?"

"Belonged to a pilot. They might know him at the gate."

Shiloh glanced back at the car, only now seeing the winged decal in the rear window. She sighed. *And he thinks I'm good at this? I don't even want to see what happens when he finds one he likes.*

"And that one?" she asked as they passed a smaller, sportier model.

"Alarmed."

"Of course. Silly me."

"I can't believe I'm doing this," she muttered to herself. Walking down the rows of a parking lot as if it were a car dealership, looking for one to steal. A nonpilot-owned, nonalarmed, nonstandout car that, of course, wouldn't be missed for a while, if they were lucky.

Great. First I have thugs breaking into my house, then the sail loft, leaving chaos behind, shooting holes in my car, threatening my father—

She sucked in a quick breath. She'd tried not to think about it, but it came back now in a rush. She would steal a hundred cars if it would get her to him. She quit muttering and began to look at likely vehicles herself.

"How about that one?" she asked, gesturing to what was almost a twin of the first car he'd stopped at, except this one was tan. And, more importantly, the passenger door was unlocked. Con halted, glancing over the vehicle, then pulled open the door. He scrabbled around in the glove box for a minute, then she heard a muttered "bingo," and he popped back out with what appeared to be a parking stub in his hand.

"From yesterday. Let's hope they're gone for a long trip." He got back in and slid across the seat, and she saw him bend to fiddle under the dash. She looked around nervously, smiling rather idiotically, she thought, at anyone who passed within three cars of them. Then she nearly jumped out of her skin when the motor roared to life; he *was* too damned good at this!

She was still marveling over how he had calmly produced the stub and paid the parking fee, then driven sedately out of the airport without drawing a look from anyone, when they hit the freeway and headed north.

"Check the registration."

Yes, sir, she snapped inwardly, but kept silent as she did as he instructed. It took her a moment to find the card in the clutter in the small glove box.

"Frederick and Barbara Sanger," she read.

"From where?"

"Anaheim." She held up a baseball cap she'd found on the floor. "And Angels fans, I gather." She glanced again at the card in her hand. "I can live with Barbara, but you are definitely not a Frederick. We just dropped them off, perhaps?"

He eyed her rather curiously. "I thought you'd be...more upset about this."

"I was. I am, really. But I'd do a lot worse than steal a car for my father."

"They'll get it back."

Con turned his attention back to the road, afraid she might read the bitter longing in his eyes, even in the shadowy interior of the car. She'd made him feel so many things he'd never felt before, brought back so many feelings he'd thought long dead, and he didn't dare think about them, not now.

He kept up with the flow of traffic, and only the tension in his hands on the wheel and the rigid set of his jaw told her he wished it were faster. He didn't speak until they were nearly to Long Beach.

"I'm sorry we couldn't fly. I didn't want to take the chance. They might be watching the flights."

"I understand." So the iceberg wasn't back completely, she thought. Yet.

Silence reigned again until they were nearing Los Angeles, with its chaotic freeway interchanges. "You may have to nurse me through this mess," he said dryly.

"Just stay on the 405 to the 101. Then it's a straight shot." She shivered a little, and he reached to flip on the heater. "Don't," she warned. "I'll go to sleep."

"Good idea. I'll wake you if I get lost."

She hadn't meant it literally, but once the idea had been planted, it seemed overpowering. Maybe for a while, she thought. Just so she could be rested when they got there and found . . .

Whatever they found, she finished, refusing to acknowledge the various horrible images that tried to form in her mind.

Con drove silently, the window lowered an inch to let in just enough cold air to keep him from following Shiloh into sleep. Not, he thought ruefully, that it was really likely. She had slipped down to lie on the seat and, inevitably it seemed, wound up with her head on his thigh. He spent several miles commenting to himself how sweet she looked, how innocent and trusting. It didn't work. If she woke up and moved about two inches, she was going to be in for a big surprise. And his taut, aching body wished like hell she would.

Knock it off, he ordered himself. She's not about to think about anything except her father, not now. And now that you've shown her what a fine, upstanding citizen and car thief you are, and put not only her, but her father in jeopardy, you'll be lucky if she'll even speak to you after this is over. Except maybe to tell you to go to hell.

Don't bother, he told her silently as he brushed a strand of silky hair from her cheek with delicate care. I'm already there.

She heard his voice calling her name softly, as if from a great distance. She snuggled into her oddly solid pillow, wishing he would just kiss her awake the way he had before. Then his hands would begin to move, to stroke and caress her, until she felt she couldn't take another breath without the full, hard length of him buried deep inside her. Then he—

"Shiloh, wake up. We're almost there."

It all came crashing back then, and she sat up sleepily, her face flushed, reluctant to surrender the dream. She looked around and saw the familiar blue roofs of the Miramar Hotel that told her they were indeed almost there. She looked at him in surprise.

"Did I really sleep for two hours?"

"Closer to one and a half." He shrugged. "I've been leaning on it a little. But you need to think now. Where can we go that's close enough to get to your father's on foot, but still be completely out of sight?"

She answered quickly; she'd been thinking about it earlier. "There's a park up the hill, behind the house. If you go to the right place, you can look right into the backyard."

He nodded, and she began to direct him in. He slowed as they passed the street she pointed out, peering down the roadway that was empty of anything except a few parked cars.

"The house is just out of sight on that curve," she said. "The park is straight up another block, on the left."

They found it easily, and he pulled in as close as he could to the spot she pointed out. In moments, moving silently in the chilly, after-midnight darkness, they reached a thick clump of shrubbery at the edge of a rather steep hill.

"You have to squeeze in behind these bushes," she whispered, doing so easily. Con had a tougher time; the stiff branches of the old, sturdy bushes weren't nearly as kind to his broad shoulders. "There," she pointed when he'd finally made it. "The one with the lights—" She broke off, then went on. "They must be there. Daddy never stays up this late."

Someone else might have missed the barest of tremors that shook her; Con didn't. He wanted to hug her, to hold her and tell her it would be all right, but it was a promise he wasn't sure he could keep. He only knew he would keep her safe, and her father, as well, or die trying. The letter he'd sent would take care of Joe and his henchmen; he had nothing to lose now. Nothing except the beautiful, brave woman beside him, who had never truly been his, anyway. He settled down to study the house.

"I wish I knew how many there were," he muttered, searching the yard and the surrounding neighborhood.

"Four," Shiloh said abruptly. His head snapped around and he stared at her. "The phone number. I just figured it out. Daddy said the number was 1704, not 1700, which it really is. There are four of them."

Admiration glinted in his eyes. "Like father, like daughter," he murmured, then turned back to look at the house again.

Shiloh's eyes never moved from him. Understanding was beginning to dawn in her mind. His earlier comments about things being in the blood and the look that came into his eyes when she talked about Linc or her father... and now this. "Like father, like daughter..."

Was that really it? she wondered. Did he believe in the old "blood will tell" theory so much? Was that why he'd been so sure she could never want him? Because, deep down, he thought he was like his father, a cold-hearted, callous man who would walk out on a helpless teenager pregnant with his child? Did he hold himself apart from everyone so that he would never have to face the fear that he might be right?

She studied the rugged planes of his face, thrown into stark relief by the moonlight. She'd known people who never let people get close to them for fear of being hurt; Mandy had been one until Shiloh had introduced her to

Jimmy. But she had never known anyone who kept away from people for fear of hurting them. It was bad enough that he had so little belief in his fellow man; that he had so little in himself made her ache inside for him.

The words spoken by Sam West's secretary came back to her then. "He who hasn't taken a day off in seven years." Of course not, she thought. Not when his work was the only certain thing in his life, the only thing that gave him any faith in himself; he was good at it, and he knew it.

"—your father?"

Shiloh came back to the present with a thud. "What?"

Con looked at her a little oddly but merely repeated his question. "Who's there besides your father?"

"Nobody should be."

"Your mother?"

Her delicate jaw tightened, but she said evenly enough, "She won't be there. They haven't lived together since she ran off with the local high school football coach."

"Football coach?" Con stared at her.

"Sure." Shiloh shrugged, and only the faintest undertone of bitterness touched her voice. "You know, young, handsome...whole."

Con winced visibly. "Your father doesn't have the corner on callousness, you know," she said softly, "and I'm no more like her than you are like him."

Even in the moonlight she could see him go pale. He looked quickly away, but not before she saw the stunned look that told her how close to home her words had struck. He concentrated on the house, and it was a long time before he spoke.

"We need a distraction so I can get inside."

Shiloh thought for a minute. "I could start some kind of disturbance out in front, or go to the door—"

"No." It was short, sharp and final.

"But—"

"You're not going down there."

"It's my father, and my house," she argued. "Besides, they won't know who I am—"

"You're trying to tell me your father doesn't have a single picture of you in that house?" he asked dryly.

"Okay, okay," she muttered, then brightened. "I know! I'll tuck my hair up under that baseball cap in the car and put on a big shirt over my jeans. They'll think I'm a boy, just some neighborhood kid who—"

"No man with eyes is going to think you're a boy, Shiloh Reese."

For the briefest second, the merest flash of time, the man from the island was looking at her from those icy blue eyes. It left her breathless, stunned by how much she wanted that man back—permanently. That was what he should be, not this cold, controlled—

She nearly laughed out loud as she interrupted her own thoughts. How many times had she been accused of that very same thing, of being so coldly, unshakably controlled? It was only then that she realized she not only wanted that man back, she wanted the person she was when she was with him back, as well.

She felt suddenly light, free. Only now did she realize the full truth of her own words. If he wasn't like his father, she wasn't like her mother. She'd known the one was true but hadn't fully accepted the other. Until now. No more would she worry that somewhere, buried inside her, was the grasping, selfish woman her mother had been. In her own way she had been as wrong as Con had been, and if not for him, she might never have seen it.

Suddenly, uncontrollably, she threw her arms around him and hugged him fiercely. She felt his arms automatically return the embrace, then felt him stiffen.

"Everything's going to be fine," she exclaimed in a jubilant whisper that made him look at her a little tensely. "I'll explain it all later. Right now we're the cavalry, so we'd better get moving. How about if I throw a baseball through the front window?"

A little taken aback at this sudden whirlwind that had materialized, Con stared at her blankly for a moment. "And just how," he said slowly, "do you propose to explain what you're doing playing baseball at one in the morning?"

"I'm a juvenile delinquent?"

"A delinquent, definitely," he growled. "You're not going down there."

"I'm not asking to storm the house," she said reasonably. "I'll leave that to the pro. But you said you needed a distraction. I can do that, at least."

"Tell me about it," he muttered under his breath. He looked back at the house. If he could get down this hill to the backyard and make it to the house without being spotted...

"That big tree in the Baxters' backyard—" she gestured to the house next door "—has a lot of good, solid branches that go over the wall. It would put you right at the corner of the house. There's a sliding glass door a few feet away."

He leaned forward, seeing what she meant. "Aren't they going to call the cops if I start prowling around in their yard?"

Shiloh shook her head. "They aren't here yet. They live in Washington and don't come here until December, when winter really sets in there."

He nodded. "All right. Can you draw me a floor plan of the house?"

"Sure."

Without another word he pushed his way through the bushes, strode back to the car and got in. Still floating on the ebullient cloud of self-discovery that had released her, she followed meekly, not really concerned. When this was over and her father was safe, she would show him, would somehow convince him, and everything would be all right. The first chance she got, she would make him see. She wasn't going to lose the only man who had ever made her feel like this.

Con was aware of her movements as he studied the quickly sketched, detailed floor plan she had drawn, but he didn't look up until he had the drawing committed to memory. When he did, his jaw tightened.

"What do you think? In the dark, without—"

"No."

She had tucked her hair up under the cap, baring the slender column of her neck. The bill was pulled halfway down her forehead, throwing her face into shadow, but he could see the wide green eyes, the sassy nose and pert chin as clearly as if she'd been standing in a spotlight. And her mouth. That soft, warm mouth that set him on fire with a speed he'd never known. Stop it! he ordered himself harshly.

"You're not going up and knocking on the damn door," he said gruffly.

"Okay." He looked at her suspiciously; that had been too easy. "I had a better idea, anyway."

"I knew it," he muttered; she ignored him.

"I'll just set off Mr. Kowalski's alarm."

"What?"

"I should have thought of it sooner, after the car at the airport. Mr. Kowalski from across the street has a car with an alarm. A horribly loud alarm. If I set it off, that should get their attention, shouldn't it?"

He considered that. "What if the car's not there?"

"It is. I saw it when we drove by. It's that red BMW parked just before the curve." Her brow creased at a thought. "But it might bring the police, too."

"That doesn't matter anymore."

"What about Sam?"

"He'll know everything as soon as he gets back, no matter what happens. All I have to do is keep these clowns from blowing the whistle to Wilkens."

Shiloh heard the rest of his words, but her mind was back on that ominous little phrase, "no matter what happens."

"The letter," she breathed. He shrugged, and she knew she was right. He had written to Sam about what he'd found out and sent it to some secure post office box, just in case. Just in case he didn't make it back to tell him himself. She wondered with a shiver if he did that on every case.

She had thought she knew about this business, but the simple mailing of that letter brought home the ugliness of it with grim finality. A brief, vivid picture flashed through her mind. Con in her living room, more intimidating than either of the hulking men he fought despite his nakedness.

Or perhaps because of it, because of the sculpted lines of his powerful body. And the scars. Only now, in this last desperate moment, did the realization that he could die just as his predecessor had done hit home; she'd come to think of him as invincible, untouchable, as she had thought of her brother and father as a child.

"Con," she began urgently, suddenly aware that things just might go wrong, and she might never get the chance to tell him—

"Let's go," he said suddenly, decisively. He tugged back the sleeve of his jacket. "One twelve?"

Knowing it was too late to tell him now, she looked at her own watch, a slim gold band that had been a gift from her father. She nodded.

"Can you get to that car in five minutes?" She nodded again. He reached into the large canvas bag and pulled out her .45. "Will your father recognize this?"

"Yes."

He was all business now, cool and deliberate. "I'll take it, then. After you trigger the alarm, beat it. Stay out of sight till I come for you." He stuffed Moose's revolver in his pocket and handed her the weapon that had been Moose's partner's. "Use this if you have to."

She took the gun without a word, mentally crossing her fingers as she neither agreed nor disagreed with his instructions.

"Five minutes," he repeated, glancing at his watch again. "From now."

She nodded and climbed out of the car. They walked to where the path split, one trail leading down the hill, and Shiloh had to bite her lip fiercely to keep from blurting out the words she feared she might never get to say. Then, as she turned to go, he suddenly gripped her arm. She lifted her head to look at him, and with a muttered oath he pulled her into his arms and kissed her swiftly.

"Be careful, Green-eyes," he whispered.

And then he was gone.

Chapter 12

Shiloh thought her heart must be hammering as loudly as any alarm, both from tension and the run down the hill. She had reached the red car with a minute to spare, a minute that had lasted at least an hour. She watched the second hand on her watch crawl around the dial in the glow of the street-light. And waited.

The instant that the hand hit the number she'd been waiting for, her hand swept down to the door handle and gave it a yank. True to form, the blaring Klaxon warning signal split the night. Shiloh backed up out of the circle of light to wait, her eyes fastened on the slice of white wall that was all she could see of her father's house.

As usual, she thought ironically, Mr. Kowalski possessed the inherent ability to sleep through his own chaos; his house remained dark. But others would awaken soon, and, irritated with what they saw as their neighbor's paranoia, would be on the phone to the police about the noise.

Then she heard running footsteps and moments later saw a large man running rather awkwardly down the hill from the direction of her father's house. Awkwardly because he was both heavy and obviously out of shape, Shiloh guessed;

she could hear his gasping breathing even from where she stood.

From her hiding place in the shadows, she saw him pull open the door and start poking nervously at any button within reach, trying to shut off the noise that was echoing off the walls of the surrounding houses, many of which were now adorned with lit windows. Giving a tug to her cap, she strolled casually out into the street.

"Hey, mister," she said in a raspy tone she hoped might pass for a young boy whose voice was changing, "if you yank the battery cable, it'll shut up." The hefty man glared at her intimidatingly, and she shrugged negligently beneath the shirt, borrowed from Con, that hung loosely on her. "So don't. Don't matter to me if the cops show up. I didn't do nothin'."

She sauntered past him and on down the street, not daring to head toward the house and have the man ignore the car and go after her. She gave a quick glance over her shoulder in time to see him fumbling with the hood, then ducked out of sight behind Mr. Kowalski's hedge when she saw another car coming up the hill.

A police car. She grinned, not quite able to believe their luck. And there was Bluto, with his head stuck under the hood. He'd have a lot of explaining to do. Her grin widened when she heard the thunk of skull against metal as Bluto jerked upright and hit the hood the moment he saw the blinking red light atop the patrol car.

A smile tugged at one corner of Con's mouth when he heard the clamor of the car alarm; right on time, Green-eyes, he thought. He was hunkered down in the shadows of the big tree at the corner of the house. He'd barely seen the movement at the sliding door in time; from up on the hill, the man just inside hadn't been visible.

As he'd hoped, the man had left his post at the first piercing blast of the alarm. Con edged over to the door and slid it open about three feet. He considered going in right then, but the chance of taking one of them down outside, silently, was more important. He leaned forward until he could hear bits of talk over the background racket.

"What the hell..."

"...think...a car..."

"Charley...get...shut it up!"

"...damn cops...over the place..."

"Charley'll handle...get back...door."

That's my man, Con thought, backing up to press himself flat against the wall next to the door. He heard steps on what sounded like a tile floor, then a muttered curse.

"What the hell? I didn't open—"

The words turned into a startled gasp, then a muffled groan as the man sank limply to the ground. Swiftly Con dragged him around to the side of the house and tied his hands behind him with his own belt.

Two left, he thought as he eased into the house. As long as that alarm kept going, he had two left to deal with. He hoped. And Shiloh was safely hidden, waiting, somewhere secure. He had to believe that. If he let himself think anything else, he would mess this up for sure.

Taking a deep breath, he headed for the doorway that she had indicated led to the long hallway that wrapped around the outside of the living room, its length broken only by two entrances to the living area, and on the other wall by the doors to the bedrooms and bathroom. Pressed against the wall, he risked a split-second peek into the living room.

It was just as Shiloh had described it, light, airy, with a cool tile floor that was practical for her father's wheel-chair—which, with its occupant, was right now barely six feet away. And, as he'd hardly dared hope, the two remaining thugs were at the front window, peering anxiously down the street at the source of the unholy din.

He risked another look, only to find a pair of cool, green eyes looking back at him. Shiloh's eyes. Quickly he tugged her .45 free of his waistband and reversed it in his hand to hold it by the barrel. He gestured with it in a tossing motion, and the leonine gray head nodded slightly.

The older man caught the thrown weapon with an easy, practiced motion and quickly concealed it beneath the wool blanket over his knees. Those piercing green eyes flicked to the other entrance into the big, airy room, the entrance that was directly across from where the two men stood, then back to Con. He nodded and ducked back out of sight.

He was running on automatic now, on instinct and training. He didn't dare think of the woman out there in the cold darkness somewhere, alone, or about what it would do to her if something happened to that gutsy old man in there.

He made his way to the other arched entryway quickly, knowing that the commotion outside would cover any noise he made. Gun at the ready, he stepped silently into the room behind the two men, careful to give the man in the wheelchair a clear field of fire. He had to smother an absurd urge to smile; the older man wore the same angelic expression Shiloh did when she was up to no good.

"You guys waiting for me?"

The two men spun around, mouths agape. One held a snub-nosed revolver, the other a nasty-looking machine pistol, but both weapons were dangling forgotten at the end of limp arms at the moment.

"How the hell did you get here so fast? You're supposed to be in San Diego!"

Way to go, Shy, Con thought, wondering with an inward grin how many men were wasting time on a wild-goose chase looking for that nonexistent house. Leaving, thankfully, only four here.

"By boat, mostly," he said easily. "Drop the guns."

The two men glanced at each other uneasily. "You'll never make it," the taller of the two, a lanky, gaunt-faced man with flat brown eyes, said. "You can't get both of us."

Con shrugged. "Try me." His casual tone unnerved them more than anything else, but still they hesitated. "Come on. I'd like to see if you're any better than Moose and his fellow Neanderthal."

Fear flashed in the shorter man's eyes for a moment, but he only muttered, "You still can't take both of us."

"Ah, but he won't have to." The voice was as smooth as silk, and the hand that held the .45 was as steady as granite. Con's eyes flicked to the man in the chair in a brief, flashing salute. Tigers breed true, he thought, and here was the one who had bred his tigress.

"Maybe you'd like to reconsider dropping those guns now?" Con suggested with drawing-room politeness, his eyes fastened on the tall man just as Robert Reese's eyes never left the other. Grudgingly, they let the weapons fall to the floor. "Kick them over here."

The heavy man, the one with the lethal-looking automatic pistol, did so, but something in the tall one's eyes flickered as he hesitated.

"Go ahead," Con said softly, his mouth curving into a smile that did nothing to warm the ice in his eyes. The man kicked the gun, sending it spinning across the tile floor. Anger flashed in the flat brown eyes when Con kept his gaze on the man, not the moving weapon. Never wavering, he knelt to pick up the machine pistol, hefting it and checking the magazine as he shoved Moose's gun in his belt.

"Nice. I'll bet Alcohol, Tobacco and Firearms would love to know where you got it. Just like the FBI would love to know what really happened to their man."

He saw the tall man's muddy eyes flicker once more and knew that his stab in the dark had hit a soft spot. He'd guessed that this was the man calling the shots, what brain there was behind Fred Wilkens's muscle; he knew now that he'd been right.

Something changed then; the tall man's eyes went muddier, his gaunt body tenser, the long, bony fingers curling into fists. Con recognized the change, saw the desperation, and knew that the man had realized he had little left to lose. Killing a federal officer had a tendency to make one's life hell. And a short hell. The Bureau did not take kindly to the death of one of their own. Con's every instinct was screaming, his every nerve on edge; a desperate man was dangerous and, worse, unpredictable.

"You want to end it right now?" Con's voice was a breath of icy air, quiet, level, absolutely chilling.

The man muttered a crude oath, his hands clenching tighter into angry fists, but he didn't move. Con carefully backed up a few steps to where the small revolver lay, his eyes still trained on the furious killer. He would give it to Shiloh's father, tie these guys up, then do what his mind had

been screaming at him to do for what seemed like forever—
go and get her.

Almost on the thought, the blare of the alarm stopped,
the ensuing silence almost eerie in its completeness. A surge
of panic swept him. Where was she?

The tall man's headfirst charge would have taken him full
in the belly were it not for Con's hair-trigger reflexes. Instead he took a glancing blow of a rawboned shoulder on the
ribs, and both of them went crashing back through that
arched entryway and into the hall. Something crashed, the
sound of broken glass echoed in the narrow hall, and Con
felt a sharp stinging at the top of his right arm.

He felt rather than saw the man make a frantic grab for
the automatic pistol. He flung it fiercely sideways; the
deadly spray of bullets that thing could put out in mere seconds was nothing he wanted to deal with in close quarters.
Foiled, the man snatched at the gun in Con's waistband.
Con brought up his knees and shoved, but he couldn't seem
to get any purchase on the man's stringy frame. Then he felt
the gun being pulled away and heard the vicious, hoarse
growl in his ear.

"I'm gonna kill you, you bastard, and then I'm going
after that little bitch who's been helping you. Her old man
can watch while I have a little of what you—oof!"

The blow he landed in the man's sunken stomach sent vi-
brations all the way up to Con's shoulder, but he never felt
it. The taunting words the man had whispered with such
enjoyment were his own undoing; he had unleashed an as-
sault that overwhelmed him with its sheer strength and violence.

In moments the man was up against the wall, Con's fore-
arm jammed across his throat, leaving room for a bare
trickle of air; his gasps seemed to echo in the new silence.
The killer's long, rawboned fingers clawed at Con, and the
hollow face was changing color as he gasped for breath.

"I don't think it would be wise to kill him just yet, my
boy."

The quiet, oddly amused voice came from behind him and
snapped Con back to the world abruptly. He shook his

head, let out a long breath and slackened the pressure on that scrawny throat. The collection of bones slid to the floor, wheezing.

When he turned to look at the man in the wheelchair it was to find those eyes, so green, so preciously familiar, looking at him with the same amusement that had rung in his voice, along with an unexpected glint of admiration and an odd touch of speculation.

"Sorry I couldn't be of more help," he said, gesturing with his daughter's .45, "but you two were rather closely intertwined."

"You kept him off my back," Con said, glancing at the stout little man, who seemed thoroughly cowed as he huddled on the sofa beside the front door.

"I don't think he'll—"

Both of their heads snapped around at the sound of a light, cheery whistling from outside. It was unmistakably feminine and sounded, somewhat less certainly, like "Anchors Aweigh."

The tension and dread drained from Con like water into sand, and he couldn't stop the grin that spread across his face.

"Come on in, Green-eyes," he called to her, his voice warm and husky as he opened the door for her.

She was smiling broadly, as if she'd known all along that things would work out. She tugged off the cap as she walked toward the porch, her hair glistening even in the dim glow of the porch light, alive with warm, red highlights. She looked at him as she started up the steps next to the wheelchair ramp.

"The cops are hooking up Bluto right now.... Seems they think he was trying to rip off that car. Shall I go tell them they have bigger fish to fry? They're just—"

Shiloh gave a sharp, pained little yelp as two hundred pounds of scrambling humanity careened into her and sent her flying backward off the porch; the stout little man huddled on the couch had exploded suddenly, unexpectedly, into frantic motion. A heel dug painfully into her stomach, driving air out of her in a rushing cry and leaving the world spinning a little.

"Shy!"

The cry ripped from Con's throat like a roar, and he catapulted off the porch to her side. Shiloh saw him and tried to tell him she was all right, but she couldn't seem to get enough air to form the words.

"I'll take care of her. Get that son of a bitch."

Con lifted his head to look at the man who was wheeling down the ramp. He hesitated for a split second, his hand tightening protectively on Shiloh's shoulder as she struggled to sit up; then he gave a short little nod. He straightened and whirled in one smooth motion and then was racing up the street after the heavy man with long, swift strides that ate up the distance between them rapidly.

Robert Reese leaned over to help his daughter sit up, concern equalling the growing speculation in his gaze. His eyes flicked to Con's racing figure, as if he were remembering the near panic on his face, as if the fury in his voice as he'd shouted her abbreviated name, that nickname used only by those closest to her, were still echoing in his ears.

Shiloh was breathing again, a little hurriedly as she tried to recoup the air she had lost. A scream rent the night air, jerking them both around to where, a few houses away, a tall, powerful figure was crouched over a short, heavy one, one arm rising and falling rhythmically in a series of blows that showed no sign of stopping.

"God, he'll kill him," she whispered, and scrambled unsteadily to her feet.

"Yes," her father said, "and as much as I would like that, you'd better stop him, my girl."

Shiloh glanced at him once, quickly, to reassure herself that he was all right. There was an odd glow in his eyes, but he only nodded toward the figures in the distance, and, as she always had, she obeyed him without question.

She had to grab his arm, to literally pull him away from the beaten man, before the violence began to fade, before the need for vengeance released him. He sat back on his heels, looking at her, and she saw the blaze of fury cool as

he took in the fact that she was there, upright and seemingly unhurt.

"Are . . . you all right?" His voice was barely a whisper.

"I'm fine."

"You're sure?"

His eyes searched her, looking for any sign of injury, not
even bothering to disguise the relief that flooded him when
he found none. It was his fault; he should have watched this
pudgy weasel closer, but he'd been so worried about her out
there . . .

"I'm sorry, Shiloh. I should have—"

"I'm fine," she repeated. "He just knocked the wind out
of me." She glanced down at the stout man's battered face.
"Which is less than you knocked out of him."

"Tough."

Carelessly he yanked the man to his feet, pulled his arm
behind him in a firm wristlock and shoved him toward the
house. Shiloh followed, sighing inwardly at Con's expression, knowing that he blamed himself for what had happened, for her very nearly getting hurt. She didn't know
whether she wanted to shake him and shout that he wasn't
responsible for everything, or hold him and smooth that
look away with soft kisses. Then she glanced up at his pro-
file, lit starkly by the streetlight, and she knew there was really no contest; she would always want to hold him.

The last of the cars pulled away, and Shiloh breathed a
sigh of relief. It was over at last. The local police had become a bit belligerent when Con refused to explain what was
going on, but when a quiet, gray-suited man arrived in response to Con's call to the nearest FBI office, things had
smoothed out rapidly.

He had also called the president of WestAir and in a few
short words had sealed the fate of Fred Wilkens. The name
of Joe Selkirk did not come up in either discussion, and
Shiloh kept silent, knowing that that was something Con
would want to handle himself.

Shiloh was sitting on the armrest of the wheelchair, her
arm around her father's shoulders, when Con closed the

door and leaned back against it. Weariness and strain showed in his blue eyes and the shadows beneath them. With a quick hug and a kiss on her father's silver mane of hair, she got up.

"Sit down," she said, taking Con's arm to lead him to the sofa. "It's been a long night."

"I'm fine." His voice was flat, tired.

"It's almost dawn, and you—you're bleeding!"

She stared at his shoulder and the darkly wet spot that stained the sleeve of his cotton shirt. He followed her glance, then shrugged as he remembered that moment in the hall when he'd felt that sudden sting.

"It's fine—"

"Right. So you won't mind if I clean it up, then," she said briskly.

"I said it's fine," he snapped. *She nearly gets trampled by that water buffalo because I'm asleep at the wheel, and she's fussing over a little cut,* he grumbled silently to himself.

Shiloh looked at him levelly. "Then we'll keep it that way." Her voice was cool, even. "I'll just get some antiseptic and—"

"Forget it, will you? It's just a—"

"If you say 'it's just a scratch' or any other B-movie line," she said sweetly, "I'll deck you right here, McQuade."

Her green eyes flashed as she looked up at him, and he would have laughed had it not been for the hot, tight knot that seemed to be forming somewhere low in his belly.

"Sit down," she ordered again.

"Yes, ma'am," he said meekly and sat.

The man in the wheelchair watched in silence but with a quick alertness in his eyes that left no doubt that his agile mind was working rapidly. He glanced down at the weapon still in his lap, that precious gift from her brother that Shiloh never let out of her hands. His eyes went back to the face of the young man sitting wearily on the couch as Shiloh knelt beside him.

Quickly Shiloh got a first-aid kit, then unbuttoned the bloody shirt and peeled it slowly away from the cut. She couldn't seem to help the way her fingers lingered a bit longer than necessary on the skin of Con's shoulder and the way she braced herself with her palm flat on his chest rather than the closer, more neutral arm of the couch.

She was vaguely aware of her father's movement as he leaned forward slightly. She glanced back at him and saw the look she'd grown up with, the look she knew meant Connor McQuade was being studied with eyes that had years of experience in sizing up men, both friend and enemy. She saw his gaze skim over the tight, fit body, linger slightly on the scars, then stop at the eyes, those eyes that were centuries old, full of a jaded weariness that faded as she turned back to him.

Shiloh finished, pressing an adhesive bandage over the cut with a motion that was suspiciously like a caress. Then she lifted his right hand, looking at the swollen and scraped knuckles, an odd light coming into her eyes.

"Leave it," Con said gruffly. "You can't help. Please."

After a moment she nodded and got to her feet. "I'll fix something to eat." She glanced at her father with concern; Wilkens's men had been there since shortly after midnight yesterday, and she doubted if he'd gotten any sleep at all since. "Then we can all get some rest."

Con opened his mouth to protest, then shut it wearily; he was too tired to argue with her. He was exhausted, aching, and trying desperately not to think of what was coming. He decided it would be best if he just kept his mouth shut for now.

After putting his shirt back on, Con rubbed at his gritty eyes, trying to smother a yawn. Then a glimpse of those eyes that were so like Shiloh's watching him with the oddest of expressions drove all thought of fatigue away.

Damn, Con swore to himself, he looks like he knows. Only then did he realize the vision of casual intimacy they must have presented as she stripped off his shirt to work on that damned cut. His stomach knotted.

No, he assured himself, he couldn't have guessed. If that man, his imposing presence not lessened an iota by the chair he sat in, had the slightest idea that you . . .

He suppressed a shiver, jerking his eyes away. He would be after you with a shotgun, McQuade. And not for a wedding, either, he thought bitterly. No father in his right mind would want someone like you for his only daughter. Especially not a daughter like Shiloh.

The thought of Shiloh and weddings together gave rise to too many ideas he couldn't afford, didn't dare risk, and he quashed them resolutely. Say something, he ordered himself as the awkward silence grew longer.

"I . . . I'm sorry I got you both mixed up in this."

He hadn't had the chance to say it before, during the cold recital of the minimal facts he had given to the FBI man and the local police sergeant, who had arrived when the officers realized they had come up with more than they had bargained for.

"I never meant to go to her."

"You were ill."

"But . . ." His eyes lifted then, and Robert met them steadily. Con sighed, and when he went on, it was clear it wasn't with what he had been going to say. "It was a damn good thing I did. I never would have made it without her. She's—" his voice dropped to a low, husky tone despite himself "—one hell of a woman."

"Watch it, McQuade!" They both turned to look as she came in, carrying a tray full of plates and cups. "Tossing out compliments so easily isn't you. Having to pry them out with a crowbar is more your style." Con flushed as she set down the tray, but he couldn't help grinning when she went on blithely, "But I did do okay, didn't I?"

"You did better than okay," Con said, his crooked grin making her heart do that funny little flip it seemed to have learned the moment she had first laid eyes on him. "And you look awfully chipper for someone who's been up most of the night."

"I am," she said, handing them both plates full of eggs, fruit and toasted English muffins. "I found out tonight that I've wasted a lot of time worrying about something I never had to. And I didn't have to get through tonight without falling apart to prove it. I realized it before."

"And what brought on this revelation?" Robert asked as he took the cup she handed him.

"When I told—" She broke off abruptly; she had no right to talk about Con's past to anyone, not even her father. "Never mind," she said hastily. "It's just that I realized—"

"You were never like her."

Shiloh stared at her father. "You . . . knew?"

"Of course I knew. How could I not? All those years I watched you trying to meet every crisis as if you were forty, not fourteen. And later I watched you push yourself, test yourself, to make sure you'd learned."

"I . . . never realized you knew." She sat down abruptly on the edge of the heavy coffee table made from an old navy footlocker.

"I'd be a poor father if I hadn't." He sipped at the hot apple cider she'd brought and quirked a bushy eyebrow at her. "Dare I hope this means an end to hang gliding, skydiving and the like?"

Con set down his untasted coffee with a thud. The pictures, he thought. All those crazy, dangerous things she did—just to prove she could face the fear? Just to be sure she wasn't like her mother in the face of danger? What she'd told him up in the park, "I'm no more like her than you are like him," came back to him now with a new meaning and intensity.

"Don't be too hard on your mother," Robert Reese was saying. "She didn't plan on what happened. She married a dashing young naval lieutenant with dreams of a ship of his own someday. She never counted on my being transferred to intelligence. She wasn't prepared for everything that entailed."

Shiloh studied her hands where they lay in her lap. Con could see the tenseness in every muscle, the emotion in the rigid set of her slender shoulders. He felt as if he should leave; this was a family thing, the kind of thing he knew nothing about. Yet what he really wanted was to go to her, to hold her until that killing tension left her. Torn between the two impulses, he stayed, afraid to interrupt the flow that had clearly been bottled up for so long.

"Do you think she would have been...different, if you'd been on sea duty for months at a time?"

"I think so." Robert sighed. "Your mother was...spoiled, I suppose, first by her parents, then, in the beginning, by me. She was used to things going her way. When they didn't, and when she realized my work was going to directly affect her life, well..." He shrugged. "I think that was the worst. She couldn't take the secrecy, the threat to her as well as me because of what I did. She couldn't even talk about my work."

"Brag about her husband the battleship commander, you mean," Shiloh said bitterly; even to Con, it was clear this was an old and sore argument.

"Oh, Shy, my girl, I know it's hard for you to understand. You have no need for reflected glory, you go out and get your own. But your mother's of a different era, a different breed. Don't judge her too harshly."

Con saw her lower her head, and his eyes fastened on the slender, fragile-looking column of her neck. She seemed so delicate to be so strong. He couldn't have left now for anything; he wanted to know everything there was to know about her.

"I...even if I could forgive her for that...I could never...for the way she acted...after you were hurt..."

Robert set down his cup, reached out and lifted her chin with a gentle finger. "Some things are between a man and his woman, and between them alone." Shiloh knew she was blushing, but she couldn't look away, she was too drawn by an odd, new look in her father's eyes. "And that is between your mother and me. And there it will stay. Understood?"

She nodded, wide-eyed. Her father had never spoken to her like that before, never spoken to her as an adult about his relationship with her mother. It was as if he were suddenly seeing her as a woman instead of a child. As if he knew.

"Good." His voice was brisk. "Let's eat, and then we can all get some rest before the sun comes up."

Before the sun comes up, she thought a little numbly. Before the sun comes up and Con leaves. She turned away, knowing that that sun would never shine as brightly on her again.

Chapter 13

He could see her in the distance, sitting amid a riot of colorful flowers, all of them brilliant in the sunshine, yet none of them outshining the burnished color of her hair or the vivid emerald of her eyes.

He moved quietly, not wanting her to see him, but he broke his silence when he saw what was cradled in her arms.

"Oh, God." It broke from him helplessly.

So it had happened, just as he had known, just as he had feared it would. She had found that phantom man, that blond California boy who walked in the sunlight instead of the shadows. Telling himself he had no right to feel it didn't stop the pain.

She didn't seem to hear him coming, and he risked another step, compelled somehow to continue the torture. The child in her arms had a smooth cap of hair only slightly lighter than the sunlit strands of its mother's, and it was tugging on those strands with a curious little hand.

Still Shiloh seemed oblivious to him, but the child sensed his approach and turned to look, a sweet expression on that open, innocent face, and wonder in the eyes that looked up at him.

Con sat up sharply, still groggy with the clinging mist of
the intense dream, looking around the room as if searching
for any part of that vivid image. All he could see were vague
outlines in the dark room. Linc's room. And the memory of
the eyes that had stared up at him from that childish face,
not the glowing green of Shiloh's, not even the brown of
that man he'd conjured up for her, but blue. Blazing, clear
blue. His own eyes, staring back at him.

Groaning, he fell back on the pillows, clenching the corner of one in his fist as he cursed both his rebellious body
and his overactive mind for throwing these impossible images at him like acid-tipped darts.

When he first heard the gossamer whisper of sound, he
thought he was dreaming again. But she was there, wearing
only a slash of green satin that he barely had time to notice
before her hands went to the straps. It slipped down her
body into a jade puddle at her feet.

She watched him look at her, felt his gaze as it slid over
her breasts, down to the indentation of her waist and the
gentle curve of her hips, over her long, golden legs, then
back to the tangle of reddish curls at their juncture.

She blushed suddenly, taking a tiny half step back. Con
saw her hesitation, her shy nervousness, and knew that she
wasn't sure he still wanted her. He hadn't meant to, didn't
want to take anything more from her; he'd done nothing but
take from her since they'd met. But he would take again
now, he admitted silently, because he couldn't help himself.
He had to have one more sweet memory to guide him
through the dark.

He threw back the covers, baring his own naked body to
her. He knew what she would see. He'd already been
aroused by merely thinking of her; the sight of her undressing for him had brought him to a point of hard readiness
that made him wonder once again if he would be able to last
long enough to give her the exquisite pleasure she gave him.

She slipped in beside him, her arms going around him
eagerly. "I missed you so," she whispered.

"I didn't miss you, Green-eyes." He felt her tense, and he smiled into the darkness. "I've done nothing but dream about you since I went to sleep."

He turned to her, determined that, even if she didn't know it now, this would be a sweet memory for her, too.

Shiloh felt his intensity from his first touch, and even with her limited experience she knew this was different. He trailed his hands over her, caressing every curve, probing every hollow, until she was spinning with the warmth of it. Then his mouth began to move along the same paths, kissing, nibbling, teasing, from her lips to her neck, from the taut, rosy peak of one breast to the other, down over the flat plane of her stomach to the point of her hip, and then down every inch of her slenderly curved legs.

She was unaware of how she opened wantonly for him as he worked his way up the tender flesh of her thigh, didn't know how seductively she lifted her hips for him. She only felt his hand cupping the soft curls, his fingers gently probing. A low moan escaped her when he found that tender spot, and pleasure rocketed out to settle in the deep, hot place that had been born in her the first time she'd seen him.

She cried out in stunned shock when he bent his head to her and let his tongue take over what his fingers had begun.

Con was fired by that surprised little cry of pleasure, and the knowledge that he was the first to show her this filled him with a possessive heat he'd felt only once before in his life, on a small ship anchored in a quiet cove, where he'd been given the most precious gift of his life.

The specter of a man rose in his mind, the man who would take this from her, as well, the man who would have this for the rest of his life. It seared acidly into his memory, and he fought to beat it back. He would do what he had to, somehow, for her sake. He would find the strength. Then he emptied his mind of everything except the slender body in his arms and clasped her hips to lift her closer.

Her shock long ago charred to cinders, Shiloh knew she was going to die, and she didn't care. She would go up in flames and smoke and she wouldn't care, because she would have felt all there was to feel.

She writhed in his hands, moaning his name on every breath. She tried to get away from his relentless caress because she couldn't bear it anymore, then twisted to get back because she couldn't bear it to stop. Her fingers tangled in his hair and she held him, as if afraid he would leave her inflamed, trembling flesh.

Her blood was pounding wildly, and her pulse seemed to have shifted, centered now in that tiny little bud of flesh beneath his mouth. She let go, let him propel her to the precipice and then, when with one last lingering, suckling kiss he hurled her over, she went joyously, his name shimmering hot and sweet in her throat.

When she could begin to think again, she wondered how on earth she could find words for what she'd just experienced. She could feel the precious weight of his head as he rested on her thigh, and she reached to stroke his hair.

The moment she moved he lifted his head, and she made a small sound of protest. It was changed to a gasp when she felt him begin again, his tongue hot and probing against her still-pulsing body.

"Con, no, I can't—"

His voice came, deep and husky, muffled by her body. "Sure you can, Green-eyes."

And he went on, and with the first flickering renewal of heat she knew he was right. The body she'd thought too exhausted to move rose to his caress; the nerves she'd thought singed beyond repair came sizzlingly alive once more.

Yet this, too, was different; each time, just as she felt herself on the verge of that sweet, spiraling flight, he drew back, until she was crying out, clawing at him, begging him. She was begging him, and it didn't matter; all that mattered was that she would splinter into a million irreparable fragments if she couldn't have him soon.

"Please . . ."

"Tell me," he said, his voice hot and thick. "Tell me what you want."

Her need overwhelmed her shyness. "You," she gasped. "Inside me. Oh, Con, please!"

With a ragged groan he rose above her, lifting her in strong, gentle hands and pulling her toward him until he was buried deeply inside her. Then he withdrew, and she reached out as if to pull him back. That little movement, that reaching out for him, broke his tenuous control. His hands went to her hips, and, grasping her tightly, he slammed her up against him, driving hard and deep.

She gasped at the impact, at the sharp, piercing stab of pleasure that shot through her. The sound made Con freeze, and he looked down at her hesitantly. Knowing he was afraid he'd hurt her, Shiloh gave him the only words she had breath left for.

"Oh, yes . . ."

With a hoarse groan he tightened his grasp on her hips and pulled her to him again, hard and fast, again and again, until he was driving into her with all the power and force his raging body demanded.

Shiloh gave herself up completely, surrendering her body to him as an instrument for his pleasure. And she found that instead of losing herself, it was as if she had won a sweet, precious victory. The grip that could have been painful only added to her pleasure, and the sounds of his body thrusting into hers, the low groans of pleasure that burst from him at every stroke, were arousing in a way she'd never realized before.

She loved the look of him as he rose above her almost as much as she loved the feel of him inside her. His face was drawn tight with passion, his blue eyes free of everything except his need and hunger for her, his muscles driving and flexing, as he sent her higher and higher.

She reached out, desperate for something to hang on to, and found herself gripping the strong hands at her hips, the hands that were impaling her on him again and again. Her slender fingers tightened around his, wishing she could add her own strength to his, to make it harder, faster.

And then it was, and she went rigid, moaning his name once more as she locked her legs around him. Her body was a wild thing, trapped in the flames he had kindled, and she nearly screamed at the exquisite, rippling, pulsing pleasure.

She heard his guttural cry, barely recognizable as her name, felt the shudders that swept his body and shook his powerful frame. She felt the hot flood as he poured himself into her, felt his hips grind against her as he arched into her fiercely, throwing his head back as his groan of pleasure lengthened into a long, hoarse growl.

She felt tears stinging her eyes at the beauty of it and held him close when he collapsed atop her, his breath coming in quick gasps. He slid to one side and she lifted a hand to touch him. She wanted to tell him so many things, but he had drained her of all her strength, and she barely managed to press a soft kiss on the thick darkness of his hair before she slipped into sleep.

Con held her tight, hanging on to her as a drowning man hangs on to his rescuer. He'd wanted to know if her unflappable control could be shaken, had wanted to do it just like this. He hadn't counted on his own vulnerability; in shaking her control he had surrendered his own. He'd never been like this with a woman, his need so uncontrollable, his lovemaking so fierce, his own response so violent. He had never given himself so completely, and it shook him to his weary soul.

Despite his exhaustion he lay awake, unable to sleep away these last precious hours. Gradually the darkness faded as the dawn arrived, and he was able to see the room he hadn't even looked at earlier in his weariness. He looked around at the shelves full of mementos and souvenirs, the kinds of things he'd never had; he'd never had more than he could carry. He didn't fit here, he thought, just as he didn't fit in her life.

His gaze stopped on a picture in a silver frame that sat on the nightstand. It was Linc, in uniform, looking thin and weary, and Con guessed it had been taken when he returned from Nam. And in his arms, gazing adoringly at her beloved big brother, was Shiloh. Her hair pulled up in a bouncy ponytail, she was the child who had worked a miracle, who had pulled a gaunt-eyed, hollow-souled man back to life. No wonder Linc loved her so. She was sweet and pure and good, everything that was sunlight in this world. And she deserved all of that in return. Not a shadowy, dark life full of grimness and lies.

Now. He had to do it now. He knew he was within a hair's breadth of throwing reality to the wind and spiriting her off somewhere, anywhere, where he could have her for as long as he could hold the world at bay.

Slowly he eased away from her, ignoring the twisting knot in his chest. He got up and dressed hastily, resolutely keeping his back to the bed, knowing that if he looked at her he would be lost. He had to take her back to her own room; he couldn't leave her here for her father to find. Steeling himself, he turned back to her.

He couldn't do it. He was going to cave in, surrender to the incredible power she had over him. He couldn't leave her, not now, not when he'd only begun to know her beauty, her strength and her fire. She moved, stretching out one arm as if looking for him, her slender body painted gold by the morning sun streaming through a gap in the shade. She was so—

He saw the mark. Dark, purple and ugly, marring the perfect silk of her abdomen. The memory of the fat man, his heavy, wicked heel digging into her delicate body, leapt into Con's mind. His fingers curled helplessly; he wished he'd killed him.

That was his world, that ugly, brutal mark, and there was no place in it for her beauty and delicate grace. His resolve returned, and he leaned over the bed to wrap the sheet around her, trying not to remember how it had gotten so tangled, and gathered her up in his arms.

Even in sleep her arms went around him and she gave a soft little sigh that settled into his name. He suppressed a shiver, knowing his body was screaming in protest at what his mind was ordering it to do, and carried her quickly and quietly down the hall.

He slipped through the door to her room and with exquisite care laid her on the bed, then tucked her in gently.

He leaned over to press a soft kiss on the spun silk of her hair, knowing he didn't dare linger or he might weaken. She murmured something again, and again it was his name; his

every muscle went taut with strain. Then he whirled, crossing the room in two long strides. He slipped through the
door, closing it behind him, then leaned back against it
weakly.

No battle he'd ever fought in his sometimes cruel, sometimes harsh life had ever prepared him for this. He fought
the trembling of his body, fought the pain ripping at his gut,
fought the merciless vise that was closing on his heart. He
bit his lip savagely, hoping for a pain that would drown out
the inner agony that was tearing him apart. He bit down
until he tasted blood, and never felt a thing.

He closed his eyes against the stinging behind his lids. The
stinging grew worse, and he felt the moisture gathering at
the corners of his eyes. He squeezed them shut tighter as he
took a shuddering breath. It didn't work; he felt the wet-
ness spill over and trickle down his cheeks. He opened his
eyes and swiped at them. He hadn't cried since his mother
had died; he hadn't thought he still could.

He made himself stand up, and with his gaze fixed on the
front door that seemed so distant now, he started across the
living room.

"Running away?"

He froze, unable to move as the chair rolled into his field
of vision from a darker corner of the room. A corner from
which Robert must have seen everything.

Con shuddered, and his jaw clenched as he wondered at
the coward he'd become when faced with her father. He let
out a long, shaky breath. Robert was looking at him, his
gaze betraying nothing, but Con could no more lie to those
green eyes than he could to hers.

"Yes." Robert's brow rose at his simple honesty, but as
if he were checking something off on a list, rather than in
surprise. "It's the best thing I can do for her."

He didn't know that his pain echoed brutally in his voice,
only that Robert's face changed somehow. As if he knew
that this was costing Con the last of his feeble reserves, and
as if he knew that feeling all too well. But concern for his
daughter still shadowed the eyes that were so like hers, and
at last he spoke softly.

"She loves you, you know."

Pain knifed through Con again, and he closed his eyes against the fierceness of it. As long as he hadn't heard it in words he'd been able to avoid it, but now the image rose in his mind with stark clarity: Shiloh on the *Phoenix,* the day he had piously spoken about her waiting for the man she loved, and her knowing, enigmatic smile when she'd answered, "You're absolutely right."

He should have known. Casual sex and Shiloh Reese were as incompatible as oil and water. She would be incapable of going to bed with a man she didn't love. And maybe he had known, somewhere deep down inside, that as joyous a passion as hers had to be fueled by love. He heard a small, low sound; he didn't even know it had come from him.

Robert reached out a hand; he wasn't the kind of man who could witness this kind of pain, no matter what the cause, without reacting. In his lined face was proof that he knew, because he had fought just such a battle himself, what was going on in the heart and soul of the tortured man before him. The war between darkness and light, between the shadows and the open air, between midnight and sunrise.

Con's face had gone beyond bleak. He had turned an unhealthy gray; his pallor stood out grimly in the golden morning light. At the first touch of Robert's fingers on his rigid arm, a small, choking sound ripped from him, and he whirled and ran to the door.

He had it open and was halfway through when he stopped, one hand on the edge of the door and the other on the jamb, his knuckles white with the pressure of his grip. He muttered something that was barely audible.

"I'll always take care of her," Robert answered almost as quietly, his voice full of the knowledge that she would need his care now more than ever in her life. Then, slowly, "But who's going to take care of the man she loves?"

A strangled groan was the only answer, cut off by the closing of the door as Connor McQuade disappeared.

Her father had asked only one question after that first horrible morning. It had come abruptly, out of a long si-

lence that had enveloped them as they sat on a bluff looking out over the water.

"He's the one, isn't he? The man who saved Linc's life?"

She'd nodded, not really surprised that he'd guessed. Or
at his tone of voice, the tone of a man torn between anger
and admiration, between dislike and respect. She knew he'd
been torn since that morning, when she had awakened to
face the beginning of the pain.

She had sat up in surprise when she saw him, barely having the presence of mind to hold the sheet over her nude
body. The sheet from Linc's bed. She had felt herself begin
to blush, but the look in her father's patient green eyes
cooled her cheeks, and she met his gaze levelly. He had obviously guessed what Con meant to her, and she wouldn't
cheapen it by denying it.

After a moment he nodded, both pride and relief showing on his face. "I've been afraid we'd crippled you, Shy-
girl. I know our marriage was a poor example. I was afraid
that my skydiving, crack-shot little girl would never have the
nerve for the biggest leap of all." He stopped, shaking his
head sadly. "And now that you have, it turns out to be one
of us. And one caught in the coldest, loneliest part of a cold
and lonely world."

"He's gone, isn't he?" she whispered. He nodded, con-
firming her fear. Con wasn't going to give her the chance to
convince him that he wasn't like his father, that blood didn't
always tell. And last night, that sweet, hot night, had been
his goodbye.

A horrible ache began inside her, but when she saw the
touch of anger in her father's eyes and knew it was for her,
she struggled to hide it. "Don't, Daddy. It's not his fault.
And he never . . . lied to me about it."

"He didn't want to go."

And that, she thought, was her sole crumb of comfort.
"Please don't hate him, Daddy," she said softly. She wasn't
sure he had heard her until at last he answered.

"I don't, girl. I feel as if I should, but I can't. I saw his
face. It could have been me. Or anyone who walks that
road."

She was thankful for that. Con had so few people to love him; she couldn't bear it if someone hated him for her sake.

Her father read her face accurately. Sympathy and admiration glowed in his eyes; it was the admiration that won out. "I always knew that if it happened for you, it would be heart and soul, no holds barred. I expected nothing less of you."

"Would you have it any other way?"

"No." He looked at her steadily. "Would you?"

"No."

And she meant it, she told herself on the long bus ride home. Not for anything would she trade the time she'd had with Con, not even to avoid the hell she was in now.

She knew the physical reminders would eventually cease, although she doubted at first that she would survive them. She arrived home to find her Blazer in the garage, all damage repaired, including the shattered windshield, with no clue as to who had done the work and no sign of a bill. She knew Con had done it, just as he had arranged for the *Phoenix* to be brought home to Dana Point long before she had even thought of it. And the car they'd "borrowed" had been returned to its owners with an apology and a sizeable—though anonymous—payment.

There had been a check for Jimmy, as well, for the damage to the loft, along with a letter signed by Sam West himself thanking him for his "help" in solving a major problem for the company.

Con had been busy, she thought tightly; while she was licking her wounds with her father, he'd been removing all traces of himself from her life with the precision of a surgeon's scalpel. She called and was politely told that Mr. McQuade was unavailable. She wrote and got no answer. She thought of casually asking Linc if he'd heard from him, but her brother had already sensed there was more to what had happened than the edited version she'd given him, and she didn't dare.

So instead, in the darkness of each night, she slid between the covers naked, not admitting to herself that it was because it made her feel as if she could just roll over and find Con's warm, vital body beside her. She knew the moment she closed her eyes in the bed on which she'd first seen him, the moment she surrendered to sleep, he would be there. He would be there, with that lopsided grin that made her heart turn over and that rusty laugh she'd sworn he would never forget how to use again.

And then the shadows would come, falling over him with grim suddenness, taking him from her and back into the darkness. It was hell, but it was all she had of him and better than nothing. So each night she closed her eyes and waited silently for him to come to her.

Shiloh glanced at Wayne, then turned her attention back to her sanding. He had found the classic old sailing dinghy they were working on at an auction, and they were stripping it down to the boards before refinishing it in the yacht club colors. It was monotonous, backbreaking work, but Shiloh welcomed it.

She'd been spending more and more time with Wayne; he seemed to ease her mind and heart as only her family had been able to. She knew he must have sensed a change in her, but he never asked. He merely used his considerable resources and active imagination to keep her diverted, and she gladly let him do it.

She knew that most of the people on the dock thought she was either his granddaughter or his gold digging young mistress, but when she found he was pleased by the first and amused by the second, she thought no more about it. And she tried not to remember when Con had accused her of the same thing.

At last she stopped, taking a breather while she smiled admiringly at the seventy-year-old man who was running her ragged. Moments later Wayne lifted his head to glance over her shoulder at someone coming down the dock. She saw something odd come into his eyes, and then he spoke softly.

"Is that him?"

"Who?" she asked, brushing a few errant paint flakes off of her nose before turning to look.

"The one who hurt you so."

She paled, shocked that he had guessed so much and paralyzed with the thought that he might be right.

"Shy?"

She shuddered at the sound of the deep, strong voice; she didn't know if it was with disappointment or relief.

"It's my brother," she told Wayne quickly.

He was in civilian clothes, and he came toward them with the long, easy stride that reminded her so much of Con. She wondered how Wayne had known, how the similarities between the two had led him to believe this could be the man who had changed her.

She introduced the two men, which was easy, since each of them had heard so much about the other, and then Wayne discreetly left them alone. Shiloh looked at her brother a little anxiously; he had dropped in at the house a few times, but for him to track her down like this, he had to have a reason. He looked away, a fact that frightened her thoroughly.

"Linc?" He raised troubled hazel eyes to hers. "It's not Daddy?" she begged.

"No," he said hastily, reaching out to take her hands in his. "He's fine. I spoke to him this morning."

She let out a shuddering sigh of relief. "Then what? Why are you down here?"

"I have to know something."

"What?" Her brow creased as he hesitated.

"Shy, I never asked what happened between you and Con, but I have to ask now."

She paled a little, but she asked steadily enough, "Why?"

"I need to know because . . ." He stopped, floundering. Her self-possessed brother at a loss for words was something she'd never seen before, and she felt a set of icy fingers start a shivering trail up her spine.

"Is this . . . professional?"

"No."

Those icy fingers dug through to her heart, and it quivered in response. "Then why? Why now?"

"I . . . got a call from WestCorp this morning."

The fingers squeezed, clamping her heart in their frozen grip. "Oh, God." She pulled her hands away, clamping one over the small fist of the other as she pressed them against her lips to hold back a cry.

"He's alive," Linc said quickly, seeing the stark terror in her eyes. "At least he was this morning," he added grimly.

"Where is he?" It was a harsh, broken whisper.

"Nevada. He was on something at the air force base outside of Las Vegas."

Shiloh erupted into motion, on her feet so quickly even her quick-reflexed brother was startled. He had to hurry to catch up to her as she raced up the dock.

"Shiloh, wait!"

She stopped, her delicate chin jutting out determinedly. "I'm going to him, whether he wants me or not."

"We're both going. It's already set. I just..." He paused, putting his hands on her shoulders. "I wasn't sure, but I am now. You love him, don't you?"

"Yes." She said it flatly, in a tone that spoke worlds of the pain that love had become instead of the joy it should have been.

He nodded slowly. "Then let's go."

They were on the plane before it occurred to her.

"Why did Sam call you?"

Startled by the sudden question after all the silence, Linc turned and looked at her for a moment. "What?"

"Why did Sam West call you?"

Linc shifted uncomfortably in his narrow airplane seat. "I... After the Philippines, when I realized he really didn't have... anybody, I asked Sam to let me know if anything ever... happened. I never told Con. I guess Sam didn't, either."

Shiloh stared at him, at this rugged, handsome, tough man who was her brother. As always when he was caught doing something that betrayed his innate warmth and sensitivity, he squirmed awkwardly. Her love for him shone in her eyes as she whispered softly, "Have I ever told you how proud I am of you, and how glad I am that you're my brother?''

To her amazement he blushed, then cleared his throat gruffly. "Anyway," he went on hastily, "Sam told his secretary to pull his file and call me— What?"

Shiloh was staring at him, wide-eyed. "So that's how they knew," she breathed.

"What?"

"We could never figure out how they found out about you, how they knew to look for me. But if your name was there..."

Linc went white under his tan at the realization that he might have inadvertently endangered his sister's life. "But...I can't believe Sam would—"

"He didn't. Con's file is confidential." She hesitated, but she supposed it didn't matter now. "There was a leak. High up. Right next to Sam, in fact."

Linc whistled. "It's a wonder he's still—"

He stopped, aware of what he'd been about to say. Shiloh heard it, anyway. "He *is* alive," she said fiercely. "I know it. He wouldn't talk to me before when I called, but he'll have to now. He can tell me to go to hell, get out of his dark, secret little life, and I'll go and leave him to his damned shadows if that's what he wants, but not until he tells me himself."

Linc stared at her, this little sister of his who had suddenly grown claws to match her emerald-green eyes. And who had never shown such emotion as she did now. "I'm pretty proud of you, too," he said quietly, and saw a little of the fierceness fade from the green depths.

When, after a long silence, he spoke again, it was to ask a question she hadn't expected. "Why didn't you tell me?"

"Tell you?"

She knew perfectly well what he meant, and he knew that she knew it. "Shy," he said, with all the big-brother sternness he could manage.

She sighed. "Because you're the only person in the whole damned world other than Sam that he considers a friend, and I wasn't going to have him lose that because my brother happens to act like a gorilla if he thinks someone's hurt me.''

It came out in a breathless rush, and Linc pulled back in his seat a little at the intensity of it. Then he reached out and took one slender hand in both of his broad, strong ones. ''You never did do things halfway, did you? He's my friend, but he's a fool if he lets this kind of love slip away.''

''I . . . don't think he knows what to do with love.''

Linc nodded slowly. ''Then it's time he learned.''

He lifted the armrest between them and pulled her into a close embrace. She nestled against his broad chest and heard the rumble of his voice.

''Really, Shy. A gorilla?''

''Gorilla,'' she confirmed, and hugged him fiercely.

Chapter 14

Shiloh knew she would never forget her first sight of Con in that antiseptic little room. The bits and pieces she could remember of the doctor's words were whirling in her mind: beaten, dumped for the desert to finish... That he'd been found at all, by a state patrolman who happened to be unusually curious, was a pure fluke.

"—no reason for him to still be unconscious," the man had said. "That's our main concern."

"Coma?" Linc had asked tensely.

"Not indicated by the EEG." The white-coated man had shrugged. "He's tough and fit, although he seems pretty run-down right now, like he hasn't been eating for a while, or sleeping. He's concussed, but there's no reason for this." The shrug again. "Maybe he just doesn't want to come back."

Those were the words spinning in her brain as she stood beside the narrow bed, trying not to see the mass of tubes and machines that surrounded the still figure.

Her first thought was that he looked so tired, with the ugly, dark bruises that marked his face and the fiberglass splint that encased his left arm. And thin. And the shadows that circled his eyes had nothing to do with bruises; she knew that look too well. She supposed she should feel gratified that these last months had been just as hard on him, but she couldn't; all she could feel was pain for him.

Tentatively she reached out, putting her hand down over his, trying not to see the needles that pierced his unbroken arm, trying not to notice how cold he seemed, he who had always seared her with his heat. And she began her vigil.

She was vaguely aware of the comings and goings around her, even drank some of the coffee Linc brought and took a bite or two of the tasteless sandwich he handed her. But mostly she just sat, holding desperately to that slack hand, tightening her fingers around his, stroking his palm gently.

And she talked. Ignoring those who said he wouldn't hear her and believing the nurse who said, "You never know," she talked. She began with soothing words, telling him he would be fine, but as the hours passed she worked up to a half-real anger, as if she could badger him back to life.

"If you want me out of your life, McQuade, then you'd damn well better wake up and tell me so, because I'm not leaving until you do. You're going to have to sit up and tell me to get the hell out of here, damn you, or I'm staying. You think I was stubborn before, well, you haven't seen anything yet."

And then, in the hour just before midnight, when she somehow sensed him slipping farther away from her, she had broken at last. "I know you don't, maybe can't, love me back," she choked out between sobs. "I'm not asking for that.... Just don't die. I can live without you, as long as I know there *is* a you...."

At last she wiped her eyes and was shifting stiffly in the hard, straight chair when the door opened. She turned, her eyes seeking the tall, lean shape of her brother. They found a complete stranger.

She knew immediately who it was; that air of authority and importance left her no doubts. She got to her feet, moving slowly to accommodate her stiff muscles, never realizing that it made her look distinctly regal.

He was staring at her with an assessing gleam in his clear gray eyes that bordered either on rudeness or flattery; she couldn't decide which, but she was in no mood for either. When she spoke, her voice was husky from her tears, yet coolly distant, and the combination seemed to intrigue the man before her.

"Mr. West, I presume?"

One of the eyebrows, a shade darker than the sandy hair, quirked upward as he looked at her. Then she saw recognition dawn in his eyes.

"Shiloh Reese," he said in a tone of sudden comprehension she was at a loss to understand. He looked both older and younger than the forty-two she knew him to be. Older in the lines carved into his tanned face, younger in the quick movements and bright eyes.

"Now I understand." She raised her own eyebrow at his cryptic remark. "I knew there was more to it when he came back. He'd changed, he was hurting, and it wasn't just Joe."

"So you immediately put him back to work." She knew her tone was sharp, but with Con lying there defenseless, she was the only person to speak for him.

Sam West looked startled, and then the gleam in his eyes began to change to admiration. "Of course," he said lightly.

"Of course," she echoed coldly. "Why give the man who uncovered a traitor for you a break? Damn it, he'd run himself into the ground for you! He'd never ask you for a rest if he thought you needed him. He thinks the world of you."

"He does?" Sam West seemed to be enjoying this, and it infuriated her.

"He does. Although it escapes me why, Mr. West."

"Sam, please," he said, ignoring her tone.

It was suddenly too much, trying to talk to this man who was able to stand here and feel amused by her while Con lay hooked up to all these damned machines barely a foot away. "Several other names pop to mind, *Mister* West," she said icily, "and that is the most polite of them all!"

He smiled, and Shiloh wanted to throw something at him. He seemed to sense he had pushed her too far, and sud-

denly his eyes held all the ominous seriousness that kept
boards of directors at bay. "Now that you've gotten that out
of your system, perhaps you could explain to me why
my... overworked troubleshooter here has been doing his
damnedest to get himself killed for the last five months?"

"What?" It was as if he'd thrown a bucket of cold water
on her anger; she stared at him in shock.

"He has never been what you would call cautious, but
neither has he ever been reckless. Yet ever since he came
back from California he's been exactly that, taking crazy
chances, running alone, almost asking for trouble. I'd like
to know why." Shiloh paled under his intense gaze, but she
never looked away. He nodded slightly, as if he'd found
something he'd been searching for. "But most of all," he
said softly, "I'd like to know why that hurts you so."

Her chin came up, and fire flashed in her green eyes.
Something was tugging at the edges of her awareness, but
she was too intent to stop now. "That," she said steadily, "is
none of your business."

A smile tugged at the corners of his mouth. "Oh, yes, I
do see now." Then he seemed to look past her for a moment, and the gleam in his eyes became a sparkle when he
turned them back on her. "I see quite well. Does he know?"

"Know what, Mr. West?" she asked levelly, despite that
odd tickling sensation at the back of her neck.

"I'm disappointed, Ms. Reese. You know what I mean."

Her eyes flashed again. "Yes, *Mister* West," she said, "I
do. But since it changes nothing, how I feel about one of
your...employees is hardly anything to concern you, is it?"

He countered her question with one of his own. "Why did
you let him leave?"

"For a lot of reasons." She held his gaze warily as she got
the oddest sensation that he was purposefully guiding the
rather heated conversation. "There's only one you need to
know. He wanted it that way."

That persistent distraction tugged at her again, but for the
moment she was still too intent on Sam West, wondering at
a look unexpectedly like approval that had joined the admiration in his eyes. Somehow it made her even warier. "Is

that all, Mr. West, or is there more ripping and tearing you'd like to do?''

He laughed. Incredibly, he threw back his head and laughed. ''Oh, you're everything he said you were,'' he said, shaking his head. ''And everything he didn't say. You faced me down better than any CEO, better than the secretary of the navy.''

And then, to her amazement, he looked past her once more to say in a voice that rang with love and respect, ''You picked a beauty, my friend, and if you let her go again, I'll either fire you for stupidity or go after her myself!''

Stunned, Shiloh whirled around. And met two bruised, battered, but utterly beautiful blue eyes that were open and watching her. This, then, was what had been nagging at her; some part of her must have sensed that he'd awakened. As if paralyzed, she stood motionless, staring at him, unable to quite believe it.

''Con...'' It was barely a whisper, yet it held all her love and longing, all the aching of these last months, all the horrors of these last few hours. She saw him blink rapidly, as if his own eyes were stinging just like hers, and his tongue crept out to wet his battered lips as if he were going to try to talk. That small movement galvanized her, and she was at his side in an instant.

''Shy...'' It was hoarse and barely recognizable, and she put a finger to his lips.

''Hush. Later. Just rest now.'' She meant to pull away, but the feel of him, of the heat that had returned to him, was too much, and she trailed her finger in a feather-light touch over his cheek. He closed his eyes as he turned his head into that soft caress, reaching for it.

''You,'' Sam said with a chuckle that made two pairs of eyes snap toward him, ''are going to be fine, my friend.'' He nodded at the machine that was registering the sudden acceleration of Con's heart rate. ''I'll go tell them you're back, and fine. Although they'd better watch your blood pressure!'' With a final grin that seemed to encompass them both, he turned and left the tiny room.

Shiloh turned back to the bed, her eyes going over Con
hungrily. She didn't know that every agonizing hour of her
vigil showed in her face, or that every last ounce of her love
for him was glowing in her eyes.

"I...didn't...want..." He had to stop to take a breath,
as if, despite the small plastic tubing that was pumping extra oxygen into him, he still couldn't get enough. She shook
her head at him, remembering his broken ribs.

"Sshh. I know you don't want me here. I'll go...soon.
Just rest."

Pain flared in his bruised blue eyes. He tried the words
again. "No! I...didn't...want it...that way."

It took her a second to remember that he'd been awake
while she'd been talking—arguing—with Sam West.

"What *did* you want?" she whispered. "To get yourself
killed, like Sam said?"

"Sam is... He talks too much." He lowered his eyes to
the tape that held the IV needles in his arm. He took a
breath, trying to get as much air as his battered body could
take. Anything to avoid looking up at the reality of the vision that had haunted him for months. "What does Sam
know, anyway?" he asked gruffly, his voice steadier now.

"He knows you've been taking awful chances."

He tried to shrug. "It's my job."

"Why, Con?" Her voice rose a little, some of the pain
slipping through. "Do you truly hate yourself so much? Or
is it me you hate?"

"You?" He stared at her, stunned. "What...? How in
hell could I hate you? I—"

"You must," she said simply, "because there's nothing
in the world you could do to hurt me more than to die."

From somewhere in the fog the words floated upward. *"I
can live without you, as long as I know there* is *a you."* He
didn't realize he'd whispered them aloud until he saw her
staring at him, eyes wide with shock.

"You...heard me?"

Meeting her gaze with his own look of wonder, he nodded slowly. "I think I...must have. I didn't want to come

back...to find out it was just another dream. Then you were arguing with Sam ... and I ...''

He broke off, swallowing heavily and then wetting his swollen lips. She was watching him steadily, unflinchingly, and his heart twisted at her pure, clean courage. She'd given him all a person could give, and then she'd reached deep and given him more, never counting the cost. She made him feel humble, not in the old way his past had made him feel, but in a new, unsullied way that strengthened rather than weakened him. He doubted if he could match her courage, but he had to try.

"That night," he said slowly, "when they stuffed me in the trunk of that car and started driving... I remember thinking that maybe I'd gotten it done this time. When they dumped me behind that sand dune, I knew it was over. I could barely breathe. I knew I'd never be able to move.''

He saw her eyes brighten with the sheen of unshed tears, saw the rigid set of that delicate chin, but he went on.

"The crazy thing was that ... then, when I knew it was over, when I knew I wouldn't have to dream about you anymore, wouldn't have to wake up in the night aching for you anymore, when I knew I wouldn't have to fight to keep myself from going to you anymore...all I wanted was to run it all in reverse, to take it all back.''

He let out a harsh, quick little breath. "I wanted to say to hell with all the reasons it was wrong.... I wanted to go to you and...ask if you still...wanted me. I wanted to believe what you said, that I wasn't like him.... That's when it hit me. When I realized ...''

He closed his eyes, wondering how she did it, how she could be so painfully honest; it was about to kill him. He couldn't go on, he couldn't slice any deeper into his battered heart.

"Realized what?"

Her soft question rang in his ears, and he knew then that for her he could cut clear through to his soul. "That I'd already proven I was exactly like him. You loved me, and I'd walked out on you.''

She drew a quick breath. "You knew?''

"I knew from the day I left you, even though you never said it. I should have known from the minute you went to bed with me."

The little breath she'd taken came out in a shaky sigh. "I... didn't want you to... think you had to... stay, because of that."

"I know. You'd never use that. You're not like that."

"And you're not like your father," she said suddenly, fiercely. "We weren't married, and I wasn't... pregnant."

He looked at her oddly. "Why did you say it like that?"

"Because," she whispered, looking away, "sometimes I wished I was." She felt his sudden tension and made herself look at him. "At least... I would have had some part of you."

He shuddered. "Oh, God, Shy... you wanted..." Faltering, he stared at her. "You can't mean... you still...?"

Her head came up proudly, and she blinked away brimming tears. "Love you? Yes, Connor McQuade, I still love you. And I always will, even though you don't love me, even if you get out of here and walk out of my life all over again. And there's not a damned thing you can do about it!"

His face twisted, looking more agonized than any bruises could make it. "Shy, I... don't deserve—"

"Damn you!" she snapped, staring down at him with her eyes flashing green fire. "I have had enough of being insulted, thank you!"

"What?"

"I happen to be a reasonably intelligent person!"

"I never—" he began, bewildered.

"And so is my brother! And if you think Sam West is stupid, you're a minority of one."

"What has that got to do—"

"So tell me, Mr. High-and-Mighty McQuade, where do you get off calling us all idiots?" He was staring at her as if she'd lost her mind. "So we're all wrong, are we?"

"Wrong?" He was gaping at her.

"Sam thinks you're the best damned man he's got. He trusts you completely when he's got every reason not to trust anyone anymore. And Linc trusts you, too. He counts you among his closest friends.''

She hadn't told him, then, Con realized. But Linc wasn't stupid. He would guess soon, if he hadn't already. And then he would lose that as well, Con thought dully. The price just kept getting higher, he thought with a stab of pain that had nothing to do with his battered body. Yet he knew that, even had he known this would be the cost, he wouldn't have changed a thing. Not even to escape this would he have given up those sweet, honeyed days in her arms. The memory of them was the hell in his dismal life, but it was the only brightness, as well, and the sweetness outshone the pain, even now. He closed his eyes against the shiver that ran up his spine, and Shiloh didn't miss it.

"Oh, Linc knows," she said, reading him perfectly. "He guessed a long time ago. So did my father." His eyes snapped open in disbelief. "Did you think they would hate you? They've both walked that dark road you're on, remember? And besides, Connor McQuade, unlike you, they let me make my own decisions. They think I'm smart enough...but you..." She laughed harshly. "You think we're all incompetent, don't you? That we're all too blind to see that you're really a worthless, no-good bastard, just like your father. Well, we don't see it. And did it ever occur to you that maybe, just maybe, we're right?"

He blinked, then swallowed heavily. "I...I never thought of it like that."

"Of course you didn't. Because then you'd have to give up your armor, wouldn't you? You wouldn't have any excuse to keep the world at arm's length anymore. You might have to break down and let somebody get close, might have to take a...a chance...."

She dashed a hand across her cheeks in a short, angry gesture, swiping at the tears she couldn't stop. She whirled away from him, heading blindly for the door.

"Shiloh..."

She heard a rustle of sound but kept going. She couldn't change anything; he would never believe he was worth loving, and it was breaking her heart.

"Shy, don't—"

She heard his sharp intake of breath and couldn't stop herself from looking back.

"Oh, God," she exclaimed and turned to race back to him. He was sitting up, his face contorted with pain, the fingers of his left hand, impeded by the fiberglass cast, clawing at the IV needles and tubes that held him prisoner.

"Con, stop." She grabbed at his hands, holding them tightly between her own. "Oh, God, I'm sorry." The tears were flowing freely now. "You're hurt, and I yelled at you. Stop, you'll make it worse, please lie down. I'll get the doctor—"

"I love you."

"—you're bleeding, and it—what?"

"I love you." She stared at him; he didn't look at all certain. "I...must love you. I can't eat, I can't sleep, and I see you everywhere. I've been walking around empty inside for so long I can't remember what it feels like to be whole. Every time I see a sunset or the stars on a clear night, I wonder if you're seeing it, too. I want you so much it hurts, worse than any of this ever could." He shrugged off his injuries as if they were nothing.

"It's eating me alive, and I can't stop it. And it's not just physical, even though with you it's...I've never...felt anything like it. But even that isn't enough. It's you I want, all of you, your heart, your mind, your courage, whether I deserve it or not. Is that love? Is that how it's supposed to feel?"

Shiloh's heart twisted inside her at the uncertainty that filled his blue eyes. "Oh, Con..."

"I don't know," he said, sounding lost. "I've never...I don't know if I...know how...." He shuddered. "All I know is I can't go on like this. I want you with me, whatever it takes, for always. If it's not love...it's the best I can do." He looked at her, and her eyes filled again at the hope in his bruised face. "Is it...enough?"

The tears were flowing openly now. "Connor McQuade, don't ever think that whatever you have to give me isn't enough. You are more than I ever thought possible."

She raised his hands to her lips and kissed his fingers softly. Heedless of his aching arm and heavily taped ribs, he pulled her down to the bed and held her close. And when the floor nurse, noticing the change in the monitors, hurried into the room, she found Shiloh curled against Con's less-battered side as he whispered something to her.

The glow of a pair of green eyes and the way Con's free arm held the slender woman so tightly to him told her all she needed to know, and despite the violation of hospital rules she backed out of the room silently, unnoticed.

Shiloh twirled around, hugging herself tightly, a tiny giggle escaping her. She stopped, blushing, when she caught Con watching her with a glint of amusement, but there was no room for such reservation in her overflowing heart today, and the giggle became a delighted laugh.

"I love them all, but I thought they'd *never* leave!"

"I don't think they would have if Wayne hadn't promised them a hell of a party up at the club." He tugged gratefully at the bow tie at his neck as he watched her with a delight that matched her own; he'd never seen her like this. The dress she wore was modest, its high collar rising on both sides of the opening at the neckline, emphasizing the slender beauty of her throat. Yet it was the most incredibly sexy dress he had ever seen. Made of a glistening white knit, it was simply, exquisitely cut, flowing over her curves to her feet with a loving grace, the sheen of the fabric alternately suggesting, then emphasizing, those curves as she moved.

She was the dress's only ornament. It needed no other, not with the burnished sheen of her hair, adorned only with a spray of tiny white flowers, and the glow in her eyes. They were vividly green and put to shame even the stone that now graced her left hand.

She'd been stunned when he'd given it to her. The big, teardrop-cut emerald caught in a delicate swirl of gold was unlike anything she'd seen before, and she knew what it must have cost. Somewhat naively, perhaps, she hadn't thought much about finances; she'd been so glad merely that he was alive, that he wanted her, that she hadn't thought much beyond the moment. He'd read her expression and looked rather sheepish.

"Sam... well, he's been paying me pretty well all these years. I didn't... need it, so I just turned it back to his investment staff and told them to have at it."

She'd looked at his face, where the bruises had at last faded. No, she was sure he hadn't needed it. He'd been used to being without for so long, it had probably never occurred to him that now he could have more.

"Anyway," he'd gone on, looking a little embarrassed, "I guess they did pretty well." His blue eyes had flashed his pleasure then. "Enough to buy a ring to match your eyes," he said. "And I think we could even afford that sail around the world, if you want."

Her throat was tight and her voice husky when she finally said softly, "I'll settle for a little cove on the windward side of Catalina."

And so they were aboard the *Phoenix* once more, its full tanks and well-stocked galley a gift from Wayne, preparing to return to where it had begun for them all those months ago.

It had been Shiloh's idea to have the small ceremony aboard the lovely vessel, but she knew by the gleam in Con's eyes that he had liked the thought, as well. She had insisted on keeping it simple, and Con had had to rein in Sam's enthusiasm; he'd been ready to charter the *Queen Mary*.

Shiloh's eyes had been filled with a quiet pleasure when Con had, somewhat shyly, asked Linc to be his best man, but they had overflowed when her father, with unshakable determination, told her that he would be on his feet to give her away.

And he had, standing tall and amazingly steady, the crutches that helped him barely noticeable. "Good to be on a deck again," he'd said, and she had hugged him fiercely.

She had gone below to slip out of the slim white dress when Con suddenly appeared behind her. "Need some help?" he asked huskily, his eyes going over her hungrily.

"No," she said with mock sternness. "This brother-and-sister act for the last month was your idea, so you can just wait awhile longer."

"Not one of my better plans," he said with a growl.

"I don't know," she said softly. "Some things are the better for the waiting."

"Yeah. Sure." The fact that a hunger that matched his own was glowing in the depths of her eyes was the only thing that kept him from reaching for her. It had been hell, keeping his hands off her these last weeks, and now the ever-present coil of desire was throbbing low and hot in him with such force it made him shudder.

You wanted it this way, he reminded himself fiercely, knowing deep down that he'd been right. He'd wanted it to be as it should have been from the beginning for her, and he would wait if it killed him.

Shiloh had been surprised, then touched, by the fact that he'd sworn hands off until after they were married. And despite the hunger for him that had been building to a fever pitch, she had to admit it had added a heightened sense of specialness to the night to come.

The mechanics of casting off and clearing the harbor kept them occupied for a while, and Shiloh grinned when she realized he had been studying.

"Just trying to hold my own in a navy family, that's all," he quipped when she teased him, and she thought then that she would ask nothing more of life than to see him like this from now on, smiling and secure. He had a family now, and both her father and brother had made certain he knew it.

It was only when they were there, anchored at last in the quiet, secluded cove, that Con remembered he had one last thing to do. He went below and dug in his bag, coming up with a small box wrapped in silver paper.

Shiloh looked at him curiously when he handed it to her; they'd exchanged their own gifts earlier, when they'd opened those from the small group that had witnessed their vows.

"It's . . . sort of a wedding present. From Sam," he said.

Her eyebrows went higher; Sam had already given them a ridiculously extravagant gift at the simple reception. When Con only nodded at the small box, she tugged at the big white bow and slipped off the shiny paper.

When she lifted the lid to see a brass key nestled on a bed of cotton, she raised her eyes to his, even more puzzled. "A key? To what?"

"My heart?" he said with exaggerated wistfulness.

"I already have that," she said softly, rubbing a finger over the new, unfamiliar weight of her wedding ring.

"That you do, Green-eyes," he said, covering her hand with his, his own wedding band glinting golden in the spring sun. "Actually," he went on after a moment, "it's, uh…the key to my office."

"Your what?"

"My office."

She stared at him. "You have…an office?"

"I do now. I sort of got promoted." He grimaced rather wryly. "I think."

"Con," she said warningly; she was about to burst with curiosity.

"Patience, wife." A grin split his face at the word.

"Feeling like a swim, are we, husband mine?" She tried to sound ominous and only succeeded in sounding deliriously happy. "Talk."

"After Joe, Sam decided he needed to beef up his security. He's adding more men to the Problem Management Force and moving it out of the main headquarters. Wants it independent, so there's no chance of anybody having access to too much information again. Or being too familiar with the PMF people."

She was gladly noting the fact that he was able to talk about Joe Selkirk's defection with only the barest hint of a shadow darkening his eyes; it was gone in an instant. Then his meaning sank in. "Moving it?"

"To Orange County, as a matter of fact."

Her eyes widened. "I thought you meant to somewhere else in Denver! Isn't this a little far? Why here?"

"Had to. It's where the guy who's going to run it is."

"The guy—" She stopped, staring. "You?"

He nodded, shrugging. "Tied to a desk at last."

Her brow furrowed. "Con . . . you don't have to. Not for me, I can handle—"

"I know. We proved that quite thoroughly, I thought." He reached out and took her hands. "It's not that, Shy. I want out. I'm tired. Burnt out, maybe. I . . . came too damned close, this time. I didn't really care then. Sam was right about that. But I do now. More than I've ever cared in my life."

Shiloh turned her hands in his, her long, slender fingers squeezing his, her eyes full of tender warmth. She was under no illusions about how little he had cared whether he lived or died, and it made his words all the more precious to her now. "You're sure?"

He grinned. "I'm sure. I'll have enough to do just to keep up with you!" The grin wavered, and he looked suddenly, incongruously, shy. "Besides, I'd . . . like to be around to play with my kid someday. If you meant what you said. . . ." He trailed off uncertainly.

"Oh, I did!" she cried, throwing her arms around him. "A little boy with blue eyes like his father's."

Con hugged her, full of the knowledge that he was holding the rest of his life in his arms. "I had a little girl with tiger eyes in mind," he whispered.

"One of each, then," Shiloh murmured against his chest. Then she pulled back to look at him with eyes that were suddenly hot and glowing. "Just when were you planning on starting this little project?"

Heat flared in him, and wildfire raced along his nerves, released at last. "Now," he said hoarsely, lifting her in his arms as he stood. "Right now."

And once more he carried her down the narrow steps, taking her mouth in a searing kiss that was at once both tender and enflaming. The *Phoenix* rode the gentle swells quietly, serenely, almost protectively, as if she had been built for a time like this.

And the small banner that Jimmy had insisted on running up the mast, with Just Married in bright letters, floated gently in the spring breeze, offering a silent, heart-warming explanation for the mysterious emptiness of the cockpit of the small, elegant ship that bobbed peacefully on an unshadowed, sunlit sea.

*   *   *   *   *

Silhouette Sensation

COMING NEXT MONTH

UNFORGIVABLE
Joyce McGill

Pat Chase went home when her only living relative had a stroke, and found herself embroiled in a murder case. Pat's instincts as a journalist had her sifting clues and considering possibilities. But who would want to murder an old lady like Libby? And why?

Adam Wyatt wanted Pat's co-operation on the case; as the chief of police he was in charge of the investigation, but people were more likely to talk to Pat. *He* wanted to talk to Pat. He wanted to make love to Pat. . .

SOMEBODY'S LADY
Marilyn Pappano

Big city attorney Beth Gibson and smart, small-town lawyer Zachary Adams met in *Somebody's Baby*, and when Zach had a case he knew only a real hot-shot could win he immediately thought of Beth. He wanted to see her again, even though they were totally wrong for each other.

Zach had brought her an almost impossible case and then volunteered to help with it. Soon they were living together as well as working together and it was getting harder to remember how different they were, why they shouldn't be lovers. What would happen when the case was over?

Silhouette Sensation

COMING NEXT MONTH

TWILIGHT SHADOWS
Emilie Richards

Kelley Samuels was supposed to be a bridesmaid at her friend and partner's wedding, but she ended up diving to the floor as bursts of gunfire drowned out the music.

Any of the guests could have been the gunman's target, but with a long list of enemies and a young daughter to raise, Griff Bryant wasn't taking any chances. He was actually looking forward to having his body guarded by Kelley. . .

COMMAND PERFORMANCE
Nora Roberts

Cordina's Royal Family

It was at the request of His Royal Highness Alexander de Cordina that Eve Hamilton and her theatre company travelled to Cordina. The tiny principality still looked like a storybook place, but Eve knew that it had its villains and tragedies; she'd seen something of them seven years ago when Princess Gabriella had been kidnapped.

Alex was the heir but with Eve he felt like a man not a prince, just the sight of her made him ache. Was she the kind of woman who could take on the duties and responsibilities of a princess? Was she already involved with his brother?

TAKE 4 NEW SILHOUETTE SENSATIONS FREE!

Silhouette Sensations are thrilling romances for today's woman.

A specially selected range of romantic fiction seasoned with suspense. You'll also find glamour, sensuality and daring in each thoroughly modern tale!

So turn the page for details of how to apply and claim more free gifts!

YOU CAN ENJOY
4 SILHOUETTE SENSATIONS, A CUDDLY
TEDDY AND A MYSTERY GIFT FREE!

Yes you can enjoy 4 Silhouette Sensations as your free gift from Reader Service, plus the opportunity to have 4 brand new titles delivered direct to your door every single month!

You could look forward to receiving 4 Silhouette Sensations delivered to your door for only £1.85 each. Postage and packing is FREE! Plus a FREE Newsletter featuring authors, competitions, special offers and lots more...

It's so easy. Send no money now but simply complete the coupon below and return it today to:- **Silhouette Reader Service, FREEPOST, PO Box 236, Croydon, Surrey CR9 9EL.**

— — — — — — **NO STAMP REQUIRED** — — — — — ✂

Please rush me 4 FREE Silhouette Sensations and 2 FREE gifts! Please also reserve me a Reader Service subscription. If I decide to subscribe, I can look forward to receiving 4 brand new Silhouette Sensations for only £7.40 every month. Postage and packing is FREE and so is my monthly Newsletter. If I choose not to subscribe, I shall write to you within 10 days and still keep the FREE books and gifts. I may cancel or suspend my subscription at any time simply by writing to you. I am over 18 years of age.

Ms/Mrs/Miss/Mr _____ **EP47SS**

Address _____

_____

_____ Postcode _____

Signature _____

Offer closes 31st October 1993. The right is reserved to refuse an application and change the terms of this offer. One application per household. Overseas readers please write for details. Southern Africa write to Book Services International Ltd., Box 41654, Craighall, Transvaal 2024. You may be mailed with offers from other reputable companies as a result of this application. Please tick box if you would prefer not to receive such offers ☐

mps
MAILING
PREFERENCE
SERVICE